Macmillan McGraw-Hill

# Math Connects
## 1

## Chapter 15
## Resource Masters

Mc Graw Hill Macmillan/McGraw-Hill

The *McGraw·Hill* Companies

 **Macmillan/McGraw-Hill**

Send all inquiries to:
Macmillan/McGraw-Hill
8787 Orion Place
Columbus, OH 43240-4027

ISBN: 978-0-02-107221-7
MHID: 0-02-107221-3

*Chapter 15 Resource Masters*

Printed in the United States of America.

4 5 6 7 8 9 10  HES  16 15 14 13 12 11 10 09

# CONTENTS

# Teacher's Guide to Using the
# Chapter 15 Resource Masters

The *Chapter 15 Resource Masters* includes the core materials needed for Chapter 15. These materials include worksheets, extensions, and assessment options. The answers for these pages appear at the back of this booklet.

All of the materials found in this booklet are included for viewing and printing on the *TeacherWorks Plus* ™ CD-ROM.

## Chapter Resources

***Graphic Organizer*** (page 2) This master is a tool designed to assist students with comprehension of grade-level concepts. You can use this graphic organizer in coordination with the appropriate lesson. While the content and layout of these tools vary, their goal is to assist students by providing a visual representation from which they can learn new concepts.

***Student Glossary*** (page 3) This master is a study tool that presents the key vocabulary terms from the chapter. You may suggest that students highlight or star the terms they do not understand. Give this list to students before beginning Lesson 14-1. Remind them to add these pages to their mathematics study notebooks.

***Anticipation Guide*** (page 4) This is a survey designed for use before beginning the chapter. You can use this survey to highlight what students may or may not know about the concepts in the chapter. If feasible, interview students in small groups, asking them the questions in the guide. There is space for recording how well students answer the questions before they complete the chapter. You may find it helpful to interview students a second time, after completing the chapter, to determine their progress.

***Chapter Game*** (page 5) A game is provided to reinforce chapter concepts and may be used at appropriate times throughout the chapter.

## Resources for Lessons

***Reteach*** Each lesson has an associated Reteach worksheet. In general, the Reteach worksheet focuses on the same lesson content but uses a different approach, learning style, or modality than that used in the Student Edition. The Reteach worksheet closes with computational practice.

***Skills Practice*** The Skills Practice worksheet for each lesson focuses on the computational aspect of the lesson. The Skills Practice worksheet may be helpful in providing additional practice of the skill taught in the lesson. It also contains word problems that cover the skill. Spaces for students' answers are provided on the worksheet.

***Homework Practice*** The Homework Practice worksheet provides an opportunity for additional computational practice. The Homework Practice worksheet includes word problems that address the skill taught in the lesson. Spaces for students' answers are provided on the worksheet.

***Problem Solving Practice*** The Problem Solving Practice worksheet presents additional reinforcement in solving word problems that applies both the concepts of the lesson and some review.

***Enrich*** The Enrich worksheet presents activities that extend the concepts of the lesson or offer a historical or multicultural look at the lesson's concepts. Some enrichment materials are designed to widen students' perspectives on the mathematics they are learning.

***Resources for Problem Solving Lessons*** In recognition of the importance of problem-solving strategies, worksheets for problem-solving lessons follow a slightly different format. For problem-solving lessons, a two-page Reteach worksheet offers a complete model for choosing a strategy. For each

of the strategy taught in the lesson. In contrast, the Problem Solving Investigation worksheets include a model strategy on the Reteach worksheets and provide problems requiring several alternate strategies on the practice worksheets.

## Assessment Options

The assessment masters in the *Chapter 15 Resource Masters* offer a wide variety of assessment tools for monitoring progress as well as final assessment.

*Individual Progress Checklist* This checklist explains the chapter's goals or objectives. Teachers can record whether a student's mastery of each objective is beginning (B), developing (D), or mastered (M). The checklist includes space to record notes to parents as well as other pertinent observations.

*Chapter Diagnostic Test* This one-page test assesses students' grasp of skills that are needed for success in the chapter.

*Chapter Pretest* This one-page quick check of the chapter's concepts is useful for determining pacing. Performance on the pretest can help you determine which concepts can be covered quickly and which specific concepts may need additional time.

*Mid-Chapter Test* This one-page chapter test provides an option to assess the first half of the chapter. It includes both multiple-choice and free-response questions.

*Vocabulary Test* This one-page test focuses on chapter vocabulary. It is suitable for all students. It includes a list of vocabulary words and questions to assess students' knowledge of the words.

*Oral Assessment* This two-page test consists of one page for teacher directions and questions and a second page for recording responses. Although this assessment is designed to be used with all students, the interview format focuses on assessing chapter content assimilated by ELL students. The variety of approaches includes solving problems using manipulatives as well as pencil and paper.

*Listening Assessment* This two-page assessment contains one page for teacher directions and one page for responses or recordings. This assessment, too, is suitable for all students but is designed primarily for use with students who may have difficulty reading test materials. The assessment directions progress in difficulty from simple at the beginning of the year to more extensive at the end of the year.

*Chapter Project Rubric* This one-page rubric is designed for use in assessing the chapter project. You may want to distribute copies of the rubric when you assign the project and use the rubric to record each student's chapter project score.

*Chapter Foldables Rubric* This one-page rubric is designed to assess the chapter Foldable. It is written to the students, telling them what you will be looking for as you evaluate their completed Foldable.

## Leveled Chapter Tests

• *Form 1* assesses basic chapter concepts through multiple-choice questions and is designed for use with below-level students.

• *Form 2A* is designed for on-level students and is primarily for those who may have missed the Form 1 test. It may be used as a retest for students who received additional instruction following the Form 1 test.

• *Form 2B* is designed for students with a below-level command of the English language.

• *Form 2C* is a free-response test designed for on-level students.

• *Form 2D* is written for students with a below-level command of the English language.

*Cumulative Test Practice* This two-page test, aimed at on-level students, offers a page of multiple-choice questions and a page of free-response questions.

*End-of-Year Test* This four-page, free-response test is included with the resource materials for the last chapter of the Student Edition.

## Answers

The answers for the Anticipation Guide and Lesson Resources are provided as reduced pages with answers appearing in black. Full-size line-up answer keys are provided for the Assessment Masters.

Name _____

# Graphic Organizer

## Two-Column Chart

A suggestion for how to use this organizer can be found in the answer pages at the back of this book.

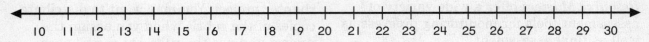

| Number | Round to nearest 10 |
|---|---|
|  |  |
|  | _____ |
|  | _____ |
|  | _____ |
|  | _____ |
|  | _____ |
|  | _____ |

Name _____

# Student Glossary

| Vocabulary Term | Definition/Description/Example |
|---|---|
| **add** | To join together sets to find the total or sum<br>$2 + 5 = 7$ |
| **addend** | Any numbers or quantities being added to together<br>$2 + 3$<br>↖ ↖ addends |
| **difference** | The answer to a subtraction problem<br>$3 - 1 = 2$<br>↖ difference |
| **estimate** | To find a number close to an exact amount<br>[Lesson 15-5] |
| **ones** | A place value of a number<br>23<br>The 3 is in the ones place. |
| **round** | To change the value of a number to one that is easier to work with [Lesson 15-5]<br>24 rounded to the nearest ten is 20. |
| **subtract** | To take away, or find the difference between two sets; the opposite of addition<br>$4 - 1 = 3$ |
| **sum** | The answer to an addition problem<br>$2 + 4 = 6$<br>↖ sum |
| **tens** | A place value of a number<br>23<br>The 2 is in the tens place. |

Name _____

# Anticipation Guide

**Directions:** Before you begin Chapter 15, distribute the Anticipation Guide to students. Read each question to the students, giving them time to answer each question. You may want to ask them the same questions after students complete the chapter.

| Before Chapter | | After Chapter |
|---|---|---|
| | **1.** What are the addends in $6 + 5 = 11$? | |
| | **2.** What is the sum in $6 + 5 = 11$? | |
| | **3.** What is the difference in $11 - 6 = 5$? | |
| | **4.** Which number is in the ones place in 427? | |
| | **5.** Which number is in the tens place in 427? | |
| | **6.** Round 48 to the nearest 10. | |
| | **7.** Is $47 - 28$ about 20? | |
| ◯ ◯ | **8.** Put in the correct signs.<br> 14 ◯ 6 ◯ 3 = 23 | ◯ ◯ |

Name _____

# Chapter 15 Game

*Adding Tens*

## Ready

You will need:

3 index cards

marker

game pieces

## Set

Write one number on each card:

1, 2, 3.

Players put game pieces on a one-digit number.

| 1 | 2 | 3 | 4 | 5 | 6 | 7 | 8 | 9 | 10 |
|---|---|---|---|---|---|---|---|---|-----|
| 11 | 12 | 13 | 14 | 15 | 16 | 17 | 18 | 19 | 20 |
| 21 | 22 | 23 | 24 | 25 | 26 | 27 | 28 | 29 | 30 |
| 31 | 32 | 33 | 34 | 35 | 36 | 37 | 38 | 39 | 40 |
| 41 | 42 | 43 | 44 | 45 | 46 | 47 | 48 | 49 | 50 |
| 51 | 52 | 53 | 54 | 55 | 56 | 57 | 58 | 59 | 60 |
| 61 | 62 | 63 | 64 | 65 | 66 | 67 | 68 | 69 | 70 |
| 71 | 72 | 73 | 74 | 75 | 76 | 77 | 78 | 79 | 80 |
| 81 | 82 | 83 | 84 | 85 | 86 | 87 | 88 | 89 | 90 |
| 91 | 92 | 93 | 94 | 95 | 96 | 97 | 98 | 99 | 100 |

## GO!

1. Mix the cards. Put them facedown.

2. Pick a card. Move the game piece that many tens. Count the tens out loud.

3. Put the card on the bottom of the stack.

4. The first player to reach the bottom row wins.

**15-1**

# Reteach

*Add and Subtract Tens*

2 + 4 = 6

20 + 40 = 60

2 + 4 = 6 helps you know that 20 + 40 = 60

## Cut out the crayons. Glue them to match the problems.

**1.** 2 + 2 = ?              +              =

**2.** 20 + 20 = ?              +              =

---

**3.** 3 − 2 = ?              −              =

**4.** 30 − 20 = ?              −              =

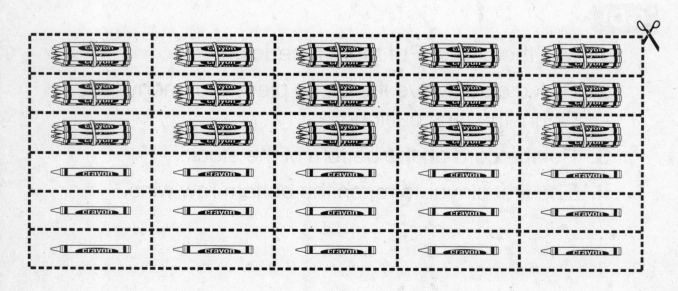

**6**

Name _____

# Skills Practice

*Add and Subtract Tens*

**Add or subtract. Use ⬚⬚⬚⬚⬚⬚⬚⬚⬚⬚ to help.**

**1.** 7 tens − 3 tens = _____ tens          70 − 30 = _____

**2.** 6 tens − 1 ten = _____ tens          60 − 10 = _____

**3.** 4 tens + 2 tens = _____ tens          40 + 20 = _____

**4.** 4 tens + 3 tens = _____ tens          40 + 30 = _____

**5.** 9 tens − 3 tens = _____ tens          90 − 30 = _____

**6.** 7 tens + 1 ten = _____ tens          70 + 10 = _____

## Solve.

**7.** What is 4 tens from 7 tens? _____ − _____ = _____

**8.** What is 3 tens and 5 tens? _____ + _____ = _____

**9.** What is 2 tens and 2 tens? _____ + _____ = _____

**10.** What is 1 ten from 7 tens? _____ − _____ = _____

**11.** What is 4 tens from 6 tens? _____ − _____ = _____

**12.** What is 4 tens and 3 tens? _____ + _____ = _____

## 15-1

# Homework Practice

*Add and Subtract Tens*

**Add or subtract. Use** ⬚⬚⬚⬚⬚⬚⬚ **to help.**

1. 9 tens − 1 tens = _____ tens          90 − 10 = _____

2. 8 tens + 1 ten = _____ tens          80 + 10 = _____

3. 6 tens − 1 ten = _____ tens          60 − 10 = _____

4. 3 tens + 3 tens = _____ tens          30 + 30 = _____

5. 8 tens − 3 tens = _____ tens          80 − 30 = _____

6. 5 tens + 1 ten = _____ tens          50 + 10 = _____

## Solve.

7. What is 2 tens from 7 tens? _____ − _____ = _____

8. What is 6 tens and 2 tens? _____ + _____ = _____

9. What is 3 tens from 5 tens? _____ − _____ = _____

10. What is 1 ten from 6 tens? _____ − _____ = _____

11. What is 1 ten and 6 tens? _____ + _____ = _____

12. What is 2 tens and 3 tens? _____ + _____ = _____

Name _____

# Problem-Solving Practice

*Add and Subtract Tens*

**Solve. Use** ▭▭▭▭▭▭ **to help.**

**1.** Lily has 5 tens. She counts back 2 tens.
How many are left?

5 tens − 2 tens = _____ tens       50 − 20 = _____

**2.** Tim has 50 crayons. He gets 20 more. How many
crayons does he have now?

_____ + _____ = _____ crayons

**3.** Jose counts 20 blue bugs, 30 red bugs, and 10 yellow
bugs. How many bugs does he count in all?

_____ ◯ _____ ◯ _____ = _____ bugs

**4.** Calvin has 3 tens and 4 tens.
How many does he have?

3 tens + 4 tens = _____ tens       30 + 40 = _____

**5.** Flora has 40 apples. She eats 10 of them.
How many apples are left?

40 ◯ 10 = _____ apples

Name _____

# Enrich

*Add and Subtract Tens*

## Read each riddle.
## Write the answer.

**1.** If you subtract 30 from my number, the answer is 60. What number am I?

I am _____.

**2.** Subtract 2 tens from 80. What number do you have?

You have _____.

**3.** If you add 10 to my number, the answer is 50. What number am I?

I am _____.

**4.** If you subtract 10 from my number, the answer is 40. What number am I?

I am _____.

**5.** If you subtract 30 from my number, the answer is 40. What number am I?

I am _____.

**6.** What number do you have if you add 1 ten to 80?

You have _____.

**7.** What number do you have if you subtract 2 tens from 90?

You have _____.

**8.** If you add 20 to my number, the answer is 70. What number am I?

I am _____.

Name _____

# Reteach

*Add with Two-Digit Numbers*

## You can count on a number line to add with two-digit numbers.

Mary buys 32 eggs.
Jen buys 5 more eggs than Mary.
How many eggs did Jen buy?

$32 + 5 = ?$

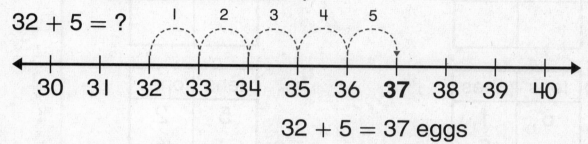

$32 + 5 = 37$ eggs

## Use the number line to add.

**1.**

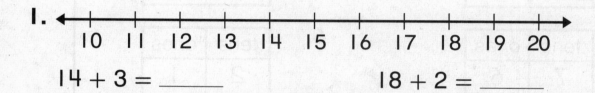

$14 + 3 =$ _____     $18 + 2 =$ _____

**2.**

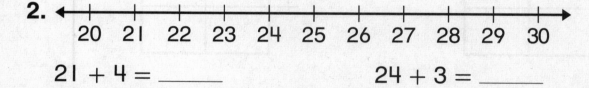

$21 + 4 =$ _____     $24 + 3 =$ _____

**3.**

$36 + 3 =$ _____     $31 + 5 =$ _____

**4.**

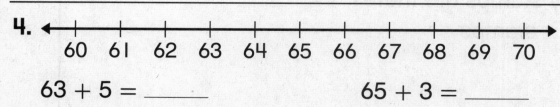

$63 + 5 =$ _____     $65 + 3 =$ _____

**15-2**

# Skills Practice

*Add with Two-Digit Numbers*

**Use WorkMat 7 and ▢ and ▭▭▭▭▭. Add.**

**1.**

| tens | ones |
|------|------|
| 3 | 7 |
| + | 2 |
|  |  |

**2.**

| tens | ones |
|------|------|
| 4 | 4 |
| + | 3 |
|  |  |

**3.**

| tens | ones |
|------|------|
| 6 | 1 |
| + | 5 |
|  |  |

**4.**

| tens | ones |
|------|------|
| 5 | 2 |
| + | 6 |
|  |  |

**5.**

| tens | ones |
|------|------|
| 7 | 6 |
| + | 1 |
|  |  |

**6.**

| tens | ones |
|------|------|
| 2 | 1 |
| + | 7 |
|  |  |

## Solve.

**7.** Bob has 33 stamps. He finds 2 more. How many stamps are there?

_____ stamps

**8.** Start at 26. Count on 2. What is the number?

_____

Name _____

# Homework Practice

*Add with Two-Digit Numbers*

## Use WorkMat 7 and ⬜ and ⬛⬛⬛⬛⬛⬛⬛⬛⬛. Add.

1.

| tens | ones |
|------|------|
| 2 | 4 |
| + | 5 |
|  |  |

2.

| tens | ones |
|------|------|
| 4 | 2 |
| + | 4 |
|  |  |

3.

| tens | ones |
|------|------|
| 6 | 1 |
| + | 1 |
|  |  |

4.

| tens | ones |
|------|------|
| 2 | 3 |
| + | 3 |
|  |  |

5.

| tens | ones |
|------|------|
| 7 | 7 |
| + | 2 |
|  |  |

6.

| tens | ones |
|------|------|
| 1 | 1 |
| + | 3 |
|  |  |

## Solve.

7. Ann says that 35 + 2 is 33. Is she right?

_____

8. Start at 44. Count on 5. What is the number?

_____

**15-2**

# Problem-Solving Practice

*Add with Two-Digit Numbers*

## Use the number line. Add to solve.

1.
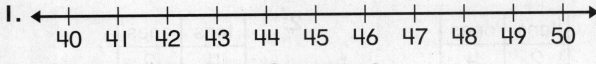
Put your finger on 42. Count on 3.

What is the number? _____

2.
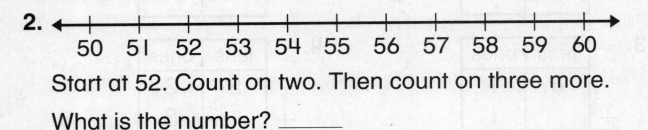
Start at 52. Count on two. Then count on three more.

What is the number? _____

3.
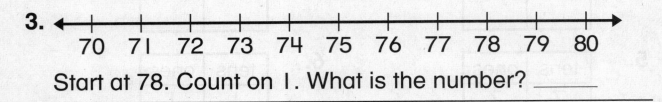
Start at 78. Count on 1. What is the number? _____

4. 25 kids are in the library. Then 3 more come.
How many kids are in the library now? _____ kids

5. 45 books are on a shelf. Jill puts 2 more books
on the shelf.
How many books are there now? _____ books

6. Mrs. Lee buys 32 hot dog buns on Friday. She
buys eight more on Monday.
How many hot dog buns does she buy? _____ buns

Name _____

# Enrich

*A Sticky Riddle!*

## Solve the problems.
## Then write your answers in order below.

27
+ [ ]
---
29

[ ]
+ 2
---
58

77
+ 2
---
[ ]

11
+ [ ]
---
19

[ ]
+ 22
---
27

4
+ 44
---
[ ]

93
+ [ ]
---
97

[ ]
+ 7
---
88

16
+ 3
---
[ ]

62
+ [ ]
---
69

80
+ 1
---
[ ]

[ ]
+ 73
---
78

What did the chewing gum say to the shoe?

**KEY**

| | |
|---|---|
| 2 = I | 19 = N |
| 4 = K | 48 = C |
| 5 = U | 56 = M |
| 7 = Y | 79 = S |
| 8 = T | 81 = O |

[ ][ ]   ,   [ ][ ][ ][ ][ ]   [ ][ ]   [ ][ ][ ]   !

## Reteach (1)

*Problem-Solving Strategy: Guess and Check*

Mr. Gil went to the store.
He spent a total of 34 cents.
Which two products did he buy?

| | |
|---|---|
| **Step 1** <br> **Understand** ▶ | **What do I know?** <br><br> The 🧴 costs 10 cents. <br><br> The 🧼 costs 14 cents. <br><br> The 🦷 costs 20 cents. <br><br> Mr. Gil spent 34 cents. <br><br> **What do I need to find out?** <br> Which two products did Mr. Gil buy? |
| **Step 2** <br> **Plan** ▶ | **How will I find out what he bought?** <br> I can guess and check until I find which two products add up to 34 cents. |
| **Step 3** <br> **Solve** ▶ | **Guess and Check** <br> I will guess that Mr. Gil bought the 🧼 and the 🦷 . <br> Check: ___14___ cents + ___20___ cents = <br> ___34___ cents <br> The sum is 34. Mr. Gil bought the 🧼 and the 🦷 . |
| **Step 4** <br> **Check** ▶ | Is my answer reasonable? _____ <br> How do I know? _____ |

**15-3**

# Reteach (2)

*Problem-Solving Strategy: Guess and Check*

## Guess and check. Solve.

**1.** Lucy has 2 bags of marbles. She has 18 in all. About how many marbles are in each bag? Circle your guess. Then check.

About: 10     15     20

Check: _____. Was your guess close? ____

**2.** Gina has 50 pieces of fruit. Which 2 kinds of fruit does she have? Circle your guess. Then check.

20          18          30

Check: _____. Was your guess right? ____

**3.** Cars in the race are 2 different colors. There are 36 cars. What color are the cars? Circle your guess. Then check.

red        tan        blue
10          16          20

Check: _____. Was your guess right? ____

**15-3**

# Skills Practice

*Problem-Solving Strategy: Guess and Check*

## Guess and check to solve.

**1.** Mike has 2 toy boxes. He has 29 toys. About how many toys are in each box? Circle your guess. Then check.

About:   5        10        15

Check: _____ . Was your guess close? _____

**2.** Todd sees 2 kinds of things outside. He sees 15 things in all. Which 2 things does he see? Circle your guess. Then check.

5              7              10

Check: _____ . Was your guess right? _____

**3.** Ella did 2 chores for her mom. She worked for 35 minutes. Which 2 chores did she do? Circle your guess. Then check.

10 minutes    15 minutes    25 minutes    30 minutes

Check: _____ . Was your guess right? _____

**4.** Make this number sentence correct. Put in the signs.

32 ◯ 25 ◯ 7 = 0

Name _____

# Homework Practice

*Problem-Solving Strategy: Guess and Check*

## Circle your guess. Then check.

1. Bob sees 2 kinds of flowers in the yard. He sees 38 flowers in all. Which 2 flowers does he see?

   20    3    18

   Check: _____ . Was your guess right? _____

2. Marlee sees 2 kinds of birds in the yard. She sees 21 birds in all. Which 2 birds does she see?

   10    20    11

   Check: _____ .
   Was your answer right? _____

3. James sees 2 kinds of bugs in the yard. He sees 48 bugs in all. Which 2 bugs does he see?

   30    20    28

   Check: _____ . Was your guess right? _____

4. Erika plants 2 packets of seeds. She plants 52 seeds in all. Which packets does she plant?

   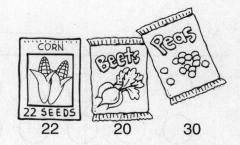

   22    20    30

   Check: _____ .
   Was your guess right? _____

Name _____

# Enrich

*Add It Up*

## Use the shapes to add. Write the addition sentence and solve.

1. △ △ △ △ △ △
   △ △ △ △ △          ○ ○ ○

   _____

2. ☆ ☆ ☆ ☆ ☆ ☆
   ☆ ☆ ☆ ☆ ☆ ☆          □ □ □ □ □

   _____

3. □ □ □ □ □ □
   □ □ □ □ □ □ □          △ △ △
                          △ △ △

   _____

4. △ △ △ △ △ △ △
   △ △ △ △ △ △ △          ☆
                          ☆ ☆

   _____

5. ○ ○ ○ ○ ○ ○ ○
   ○ ○ ○ ○ ○ ○ ○ ○

   _____

Name _____

# Reteach

*Add Two-Digit Numbers*

## You can use a number line to add ones or tens.

Lu plants 23 flowers. Meg plants 35 flowers.
How many flowers are there now?

$23 + 35 = ?$

**Count on by ones to add one.**
**Start with the greater number.**

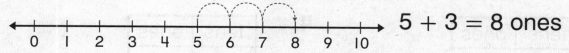

$5 + 3 = 8$ ones

**Count on by tens to add ten.**
**Start with the greater number.**

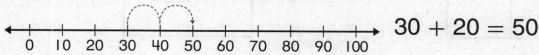

$30 + 20 = 50$

50 tens and 8 ones $= 58$ flowers

---

## Use the number lines to add ones and tens.

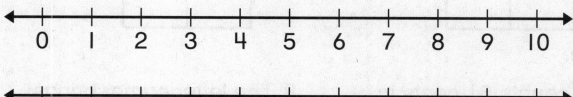

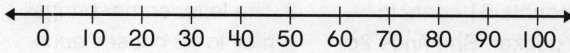

**1.** $42 + 24 =$ _____

**2.** $78 + 11 =$ _____

**3.** $31 + 52 =$ _____

**4.** $15 + 14 =$ _____

Name _____

# Skills Practice

*Add Two-Digit Numbers*

## Use WorkMat 7 and ▱ and ▭▭▭▭▭▭▭▭▭. Add.

**1.**

| tens | ones |
|------|------|
| 3 | 7 |
| + 1 | 2 |
|  |  |

**2.**

| tens | ones |
|------|------|
| 5 | 0 |
| + 3 | 3 |
|  |  |

**3.**

| tens | ones |
|------|------|
| 1 | 7 |
| + 6 | 2 |
|  |  |

**4.**

| tens | ones |
|------|------|
| 3 | 5 |
| + 2 | 3 |
|  |  |

**5.**

| tens | ones |
|------|------|
| 7 | 7 |
| + 2 | 2 |
|  |  |

**6.**

| tens | ones |
|------|------|
| 3 | 4 |
| + 1 | 5 |
|  |  |

## Solve.

**7.** Lu counts 51 cents in her pocket. She finds 26 more. How many cents does she have now?

_____

**8.** The letter carrier brings mail to 13 houses each day. How many houses does he visit in 2 days?

_____

Name _____

# Homework Practice

*Add Two-Digit Numbers*

## Use WorkMat 7 and ▢ and ▭▭▭▭▭▭. Add.

**1.**

| tens | ones |
|------|------|
| 2 | 5 |
| + 4 | 2 |
|  |  |

**2.**

| tens | ones |
|------|------|
| 5 | 6 |
| + 1 | 3 |
|  |  |

**3.**

| tens | ones |
|------|------|
| 3 | 5 |
| + 1 | 1 |
|  |  |

**4.**

| tens | ones |
|------|------|
| 7 | 3 |
| + 2 | 2 |
|  |  |

**5.**

| tens | ones |
|------|------|
| 2 | 0 |
| + 3 | 4 |
|  |  |

**6.**

| tens | ones |
|------|------|
| 8 | 1 |
| + 1 | 0 |
|  |  |

## Solve.

**7.** Sam has 31 blocks. A friend gives her 26 more. How many blocks does she have in all?

_____ blocks

**8.** Bob made 14 cookies for a bake sale. Mary made 25. How many cookies did they make?

_____ cookies

**15-4**

# Problem-Solving Practice

*Add Two-Digit Numbers*

**Solve.**

1. Mac walks 12 blocks to school. Jody walks 14 blocks. How many blocks do they walk in all?

   _____ + _____ = _____ blocks

2. Raul has 21 toy cars. He gets a set of 35 cars for his birthday. How many cars does he have now?

   _____ + _____ = _____ cars

3. 44 frogs, 21 fish, and 23 bugs live in a pond. How many bugs and frogs are there?

   _____ bugs and frogs

4. One farm has 21 pigs. The other farm has 44 pigs. How many pigs are there in all?

   _____ + _____ = _____ pigs

5. Rosa finds 36 ants outside. She finds 11 more in the shed. How many ants does she find?

   _____ ants

6. Leo has 13 red crayons, 24 blue crayons, and 45 yellow crayons. How many blue and yellow crayons does Leo have?

   _____ blue and yellow crayons

Name _____

# Enrich

*Get Well Greetings*

**Ms. Reed's first grade class is making cards for people in the local hospital. Use the clues to find out how many cards are made.**

1. Tara uses glitter to make 24 cards.
   Seth uses the computer to make his cards.
   He makes 21 more cards than Tara makes.
   How many cards does Seth make?

   _____ cards

2. Cole paints 12 cards.
   Tom uses markers to make 27 cards.
   How many cards do they make together?

   _____ cards

3. Kim and Mae both use colored pencils
   to make a total of 50 cards.
   If Kim makes 29 cards,
   how many does Mae make?

   $29 + \underline{\hspace{1cm}} = 50$ cards

4. Brady uses markers to draw his cards.
   Mia uses stamps to make her 32 cards.
   If Brady and Mia make 49 cards together,
   how many cards does Brady make?

   $32 + \underline{\hspace{1cm}} = 49$ cards

**15-5**

# Reteach

*Estimate Sums*

**If you do not need an exact sum, you can estimate.**
**If a number ends in 0, 1, 2, 3, or 4, you can round down.**
**If a number ends in 5, 6, 7, 8, or 9, you can round up.**

What is $33 + 19$?

33 is about the same as 30.

19 is about the same as 20.

$30 + 20 = 50$, so the exact sum of $33 + 19$ will be about 50.

---

**Round each number to the nearest *ten*. Then add.**

**1.** 59 rounds to _____        32 rounds to _____

   59 + 32 is about _____        _____ + _____ = _____

**2.** 44 rounds to _____        13 rounds to _____

   44 + 13 is about _____        _____ + _____ = _____

**3.** 38 rounds to _____        21 rounds to _____

   38 + 21 is about _____        _____ + _____ = _____

**4.** 41 rounds to _____        43 rounds to _____

   41 + 43 is about _____        _____ + _____ = _____

Name _____

# Skills Practice

*Estimate Sums*

**Round to the nearest *ten*. Then add.**
**Use the number lines to help.**

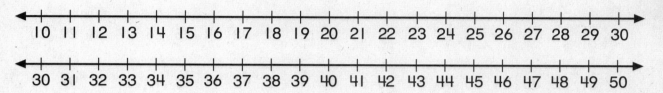

**1.** $47 + 29$

47 rounds to _____

29 rounds to _____

_____ + _____ = _____

**2.** $22 + 13$

22 rounds to _____

13 rounds to _____

_____ + _____ = _____

**3.** $24 + 28$

_____ + _____ = _____

**4.** $39 + 17$

_____ + _____ = _____

**5.** $33 + 11$

_____ + _____ = _____

**6.** $31 + 42$

_____ + _____ = _____

## Solve.

**7.** Lee had 21 stickers. She gets 11 more. About how many does she have now?

_____ + _____ = _____ She has about _____ stickers.

**8.** Tom had 62 marbles. His sister gives him 25 more. About how many marbles does he have now?

_____ + _____ = _____ He has about _____ marbles.

Name _____

# Homework Practice

*Estimate Sums*

**Round to the nearest *ten*. Then add.**
**Use the number lines to help.**

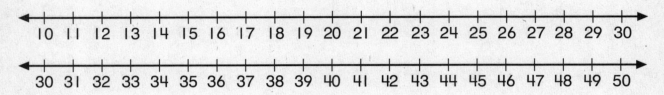

**1.** 33 + 19

33 rounds to _____

19 rounds to _____

_____ + _____ = _____

**2.** 41 + 41

41 rounds to _____

41 rounds to _____

_____ + _____ = _____

**3.** 34 + 18

_____ + _____ = _____

**4.** 26 + 34

_____ + _____ = _____

**5.** 23 + 47

_____ + _____ = _____

**6.** 28 + 19

_____ + _____ = _____

**Solve.**

**7.** Mark has 18 cents. He finds 33 more in his desk.
About how much does he have now?

_____ + _____ = _____ He has about _____ cents.

**8.** Chet's mom gives him 16 pennies. His dad gives him
19. Chet says he has about 40 pennies.
Is he right? _____ How do you know? _____ + _____ =

**15-5**

# Problem-Solving Practice

*Estimate Sums*

## Estimate to solve.

1. Mr. Smith has 11 cents. Mrs. Smith has 19 cents. About how much do they have?

   _____ + _____ = _____   They have about _____ cents.

2. Mike's dad got 29 letters this week. He got 21 letters last week. About how many letters did he get?

   _____ + _____ = _____   He got about _____ letters.

3. Ella found 9 acorns in the yard. She found 27 acorns at the park. She says she has about 30 acorns.

   Is she right? _____   How do you know? ____ + ____ = ____

4. Mike has 9 cents. Rita has 31 cents. About how much do they have?

   _____ + _____ = _____   They have about _____ cents.

5. Suzie looked at the pictures in 24 books last month. She looked at 19 books this month. About how many books has she looked at?

   _____ + _____ = _____

   She looked at about _____ books.

Name _____

# Enrich

*A Cheesy Situation*

Help Moe the mouse get each piece of cheese
to its mouse hole. Round to solve the problems.
Draw a line to the correct sum.

70    60    40    80    90

| 13 +33 | 42 +36 | 32 +34 | 76 +12 | 46 +21 |

Name _____

# Reteach

*Subtract with Two-Digit Numbers*

You can count back on a number line to subtract from two-digit numbers.

Larry has 28 stamps. He uses 5 of them.

How many stamps are left?

$28 - 5 = ?$

Start at the greater number and count back.

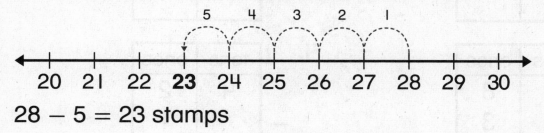

$28 - 5 = 23$ stamps

## Use the number line to subtract.

**1.**
$$\begin{array}{r} 15 \\ -\ 4 \\ \hline \end{array}$$

| | | | | | | | | | | |
|10|11|12|13|14|15|16|17|18|19|20|

**2.**
$$\begin{array}{r} 29 \\ -\ 2 \\ \hline \end{array}$$

| | | | | | | | | | | |
|20|21|22|23|24|25|26|27|28|29|30|

**3.**
$$\begin{array}{r} 38 \\ -\ 6 \\ \hline \end{array}$$

| | | | | | | | | | | |
|30|31|32|33|34|35|36|37|38|39|40|

**4.**
$$\begin{array}{r} 57 \\ -\ 7 \\ \hline \end{array}$$

| | | | | | | | | | | |
|50|51|52|53|54|55|56|57|58|59|60|

## 15-6 | Skills Practice

*Subtract with Two-Digit Numbers*

**Use WorkMat 7 and ⬜ and ▭▭▭▭. Subtract.**

1.

| tens | ones |
|------|------|
| 2 | 6 |
| − | 5 |
|  |  |

2.

| tens | ones |
|------|------|
| 4 | 9 |
| − | 6 |
|  |  |

3.

| tens | ones |
|------|------|
| 1 | 8 |
| − | 3 |
|  |  |

4.

| tens | ones |
|------|------|
| 4 | 2 |
| − | 1 |
|  |  |

5.

| tens | ones |
|------|------|
| 7 | 7 |
| − | 5 |
|  |  |

6.

| tens | ones |
|------|------|
| 3 | 5 |
| − | 2 |
|  |  |

## Solve.

7. Ann has 28 paper dolls. She gives 6 to her friends. How many does she have now?

_____ paper dolls

8. Start at 39. Count back 4. What is the number?

_____

Name _____

# Homework Practice

*Subtract with Two-Digit Numbers*

## Use WorkMat 7 and ☐ and ▭▭▭▭▭▭▭. Subtract.

1.

| tens | ones |
|------|------|
| 1    | 5    |
| −    | 4    |
|      |      |

2.

| tens | ones |
|------|------|
| 3    | 8    |
| −    | 5    |
|      |      |

3.

| tens | ones |
|------|------|
| 2    | 8    |
| −    | 4    |
|      |      |

4.

| tens | ones |
|------|------|
| 3    | 6    |
| −    | 2    |
|      |      |

5.

| tens | ones |
|------|------|
| 8    | 8    |
| −    | 4    |
|      |      |

6.

| tens | ones |
|------|------|
| 3    | 7    |
| −    | 3    |
|      |      |

## Solve.

7. Jon got 28 points in football.
   Rosa got 7 fewer points than Jon.
   How many points did Rosa get? _____ points
   How many points did Rosa and Jon get altogether?
   _____ points

**15-6**

# Problem-Solving Strategy

*Subtract with Two-Digit Numbers*

## Subtract to solve. Use the number lines.

**1.** Put your finger on 67. Count back 4.
What is the number? _____

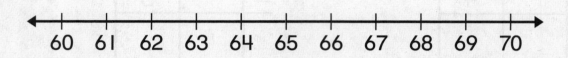

60  61  62  63  64  65  66  67  68  69  70

**2.** Jim starts at 29. He counts back four. Then he counts
back four more. What is Jim's number? _____

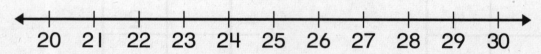

20  21  22  23  24  25  26  27  28  29  30

**3.** Lori starts at 24. She counts back 2. What is Lori's
number? _____

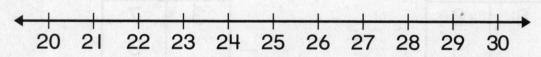

20  21  22  23  24  25  26  27  28  29  30

**4.** Jake has 47 baseball cards. He gives 5 to his friends.
How many cards are left? _____ cards

**5.** Tina is 48 inches tall. Her brother is 6 inches shorter
than Tina. How tall is Tina's brother? _____ inches tall

**6.** Mr. Watson made 39 sandwiches. He sold three on the
first day. He sold four on the second day. How many
sandwiches does he have left? _____ sandwiches

Name _____

# Enrich

*A Harey Problem!*

## The bunny has to solve all of the subtraction problems to get to the carrot. Can you help?

| | | | |
|---|---|---|---|
| (bunny) | 26<br>− ☐<br>22 | ☐<br>− 2<br>46 | 17<br>− 3<br>☐ |
| 49<br>− ☐<br>45 | ☐<br>− 5<br>33 | 48<br>− 6<br>☐ | 79<br>− 3<br>☐ |
| ☐<br>− 2<br>77 | 18<br>− 3<br>☐ | 44<br>− ☐<br>40 | ☐<br>− 6<br>92 |
| 34<br>− ☐<br>32 | ☐<br>− 1<br>92 | 46<br>− 3<br>☐ | 58<br>− ☐<br>50 |
| 66<br>− 4<br>☐ | 45<br>− ☐<br>42 | 72<br>− 1<br>☐ | ☐<br>− 6<br>82 |
| 26<br>− 2<br>☐ | ☐<br>− 4<br>52 | 58<br>− ☐<br>53 | (carrot) |

# 15-7

# Reteach

*Subtract Two-Digit Numbers*

68 birds are in a tree. 47 fly away.
How many birds stay in the tree?

68 − 47 = ?

**Count back by ones to subtract one.**

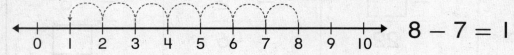 8 − 7 = 1

**Count back by tens to subtract ten.**

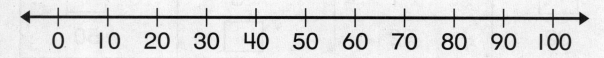 60 − 40 = 20

20 and 1 = 21 birds

---

**Use the number lines to subtract tens and ones.**

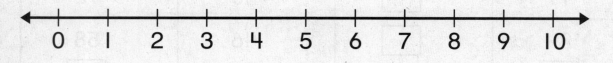

**1.** 78 − 17 = _____          **2.** 38 − 15 = _____

**3.** 49 − 19 = _____          **4.** 76 − 33 = _____

**5.** 57 − 22 = _____          **6.** 65 − 21 = _____

Name _____

# Skills Practice

## Subtract Two-Digit Numbers

**Use WorkMat 7 and ⬜ and ▭▭▭▭▭▭. Subtract.**

**1.**

| tens | ones |
|------|------|
| 5 | 7 |
| − 1 | 5 |
|      |      |

**2.**

| tens | ones |
|------|------|
| 3 | 9 |
| − 2 | 3 |
|      |      |

**3.**

| tens | ones |
|------|------|
| 4 | 7 |
| − 3 | 4 |
|      |      |

**4.**

| tens | ones |
|------|------|
| 6 | 4 |
| − 3 | 1 |
|      |      |

**5.**

| tens | ones |
|------|------|
| 8 | 3 |
| − 1 | 1 |
|      |      |

**6.**

| tens | ones |
|------|------|
| 9 | 5 |
| − 1 | 3 |
|      |      |

## Solve.

**7.** Jeff bought 38 cherries. He gave 23 to his dad. How many cherries are left?

_____ cherries

**8.** Marge counted 59 leaves on a tree. She counts 31 the next day. How many leaves fell off the tree?

_____ leaves

Name _____

# Homework Practice

*Subtract Two-Digit Numbers*

## Use WorkMat 7 and ▢ and ▭▭▭▭▭. Subtract.

**1.**

| tens | ones |
|------|------|
| 4 | 7 |
| − 2 | 3 |
|  |  |

**2.**

| tens | ones |
|------|------|
| 2 | 9 |
| − 1 | 2 |
|  |  |

**3.**

| tens | ones |
|------|------|
| 4 | 2 |
| − 1 | 1 |
|  |  |

**4.**

| tens | ones |
|------|------|
| 7 | 8 |
| − 5 | 5 |
|  |  |

**5.**

| tens | ones |
|------|------|
| 6 | 6 |
| − 5 | 3 |
|  |  |

**6.**

| tens | ones |
|------|------|
| 2 | 7 |
| − 1 | 6 |
|  |  |

## Solve.

**7.** Eva found 57 pennies. She keeps 25. How many pennies does she give away?

_____ pennies

**8.** Rick picked 59 apples. He sells 36. How many apples are left?

_____ apples

**15-7**

# Problem-Solving Practice

*Subtract Two-Digit Numbers*

## Subtract to solve.

1. Tia is 49 inches tall. Her brother is 35 inches tall.
   How much taller is Tia?

   _____ – _____ = _____

   Tia is _____ inches taller than her brother.

2. Jill has 56 coins. She loses 22 of them.
   How many coins are left? _____ coins

3. 63 crows sit on a fence. 30 fly away. Then 21 more fly
   away. How many crows are still on the fence? _____

4. Paco runs for 39 minutes. His sister runs for
   11 minutes. How many more minutes does Paco run?

   _____ – _____ = _____

   Paco runs for _____ more minutes than his sister.

5. A library has 67 books. 42 books are checked out.
   How many books are left? _____ books

6. Ms. May has 88 cents. She gives 13 cents to her son.
   She gives 25 cents to her daughter. How much does
   Ms. May have left? _____ cents

Name _____

# Enrich

*Domino Subtraction*

**Play a game of Domino Subtraction.**
**Put your  facedown.**
**Turn over 1 .**
**Make a subtraction sentence subtracting**
**the little number from the big number.**
**Add to check.**

$$\begin{array}{r} 6 \\ -\ 4 \\ \hline 2 \end{array} \qquad \begin{array}{r} 4 \\ +\ 2 \\ \hline 6 \end{array}$$

**1.** ☐ − ☐ = ☐      ☐ + ☐ = ☐

**2.** ☐ − ☐ = ☐      ☐ + ☐ = ☐

**3.** ☐ − ☐ = ☐      ☐ + ☐ = ☐

**4.** ☐ − ☐ = ☐      ☐ + ☐ = ☐

**5.** ☐ − ☐ = ☐      ☐ + ☐ = ☐

**6.** ☐ − ☐ = ☐      ☐ + ☐ = ☐

Name _____

# Reteach (1)

*Problem-Solving Investigation: Choose a Strategy*

There are 54 dogs and 32 cats at the pet store.
How many more dogs are in the store than cats?

| Step 1 Understand | **What do I know?** There are 54 dogs. There are 32 cats. **What do I need to find out?** How many more dogs are there than cats? |
|---|---|
| Step 2 Plan | **How will I find out?** I can guess and check. But I may not guess the answer right away. Making a table might be easier. I will make a table. |
| Step 3 Solve | **Make a table.** |

| Pets | Tens | Ones |
|---|---|---|
| Dogs | 50 | 4 |
| Cats | 30 | 2 |

There are _____ more dogs than cats.

| Step 4 Check | Does my table show how many more dogs there are? _____ Did I choose a good strategy? _____ |
|---|---|

**15-8**

# Reteach (2)

*Problem-Solving Investigation: Choose a Strategy*

**Choose a strategy and solve.**

| Problem Solving Strategies |
| --- |
| • Guess and check |
| • Choose the operation |
| • Make a table |

**1.** Frank rakes 10 yards. Mike rakes 5. How many yards do they rake in all?

_____ yards

**2.** Stan rides his bike for 32 yards. Lee rides her bike for 56 yards. How many more yards does Lee ride than Stan?

_____ yards

**3.** James sees 2 kinds of flowers in his yard. He sees 40 in all. Which 2 flowers does he see? Circle your answer.

31

9

20

**4.** Meg gives 20 cents to her brother. She gives 34 cents to her sister. She has 11 cents left. How much money does she start with?

_____ cents

**42**

**15-8**

# Skills Practice

*Problem-Solving Investigation: Choose a Strategy*

## Choose a strategy and solve.

| **Problem Solving Strategies** |
| --- |
| • Guess and check |
| • Choose the operation |
| • Make a table |

1. Lin plants 12 seeds. Dee plants 34 seeds. How many seeds do they plant?

   _____ seeds

2. Raul has 10 toy cars. He gets a set of 30 cars for his birthday. How many cars does he have now? _____ cars

3. Lita sees two kinds of objects on her trip. She sees 39 in all. Which two objects does she see? Circle your answer.

   15          18          21

4. The letter carrier brings mail to 20 homes on Lee Street. He brings mail to 10 homes on Main Street. How many homes is that?

   _____ homes

5. Jen's block has 48 trees. Sam's block has 23 trees. How many more trees are on Jen's block?

   _____ trees

6. Lou has 16 shirts. Greg has 11 shirts. About how many shirts do they have? Round to the nearest ten.

   About _____ shirts

**43**

Name _____

# Homework Practice

*Problem-Solving Investigation: Choose a Strategy*

**Choose a strategy and solve.**

| Problem Solving Strategies |
| --- |
| • Guess and check |
| • Choose the operation |
| • Make a table |

1. Nick's teddy bear is 22 inches high. Fred's teddy bear is 10 inches high. How many inches taller is Nick's teddy bear?

   _____ inches

2. The classroom is 35 feet long. A shelf is 3 feet long. How much longer is the classroom than the shelf?

   _____ feet

3. Lisa has 32 marbles. Tim has 41 marbles. About how many marbles do they have? Round.

   About _____ marbles

4. Mr. Lin spends 40 cents at the store. He buys 2 objects. What does Mr. Lin buy? Circle your answer.

5. 21 birds are in a field. 18 more fly in. How many birds are there now?

   _____ birds

6. Jan has 12 red stickers and 31 yellow stickers. About how many stickers does she have? Round.

   About _____ stickers

Name _____

# Enrich

*Subtraction Stories*

## Read the story. Draw a picture. Write a subtraction sentence to solve.

1. There are 11 bones and 3 dogs. How many more bones are there than dogs?

_____

2. There are 12 balloons. 6 balloons pop. How many balloons are left?

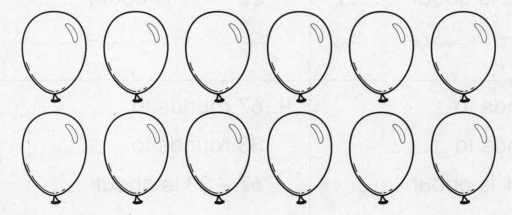

_____

**15-9**

# Reteach

*Estimate Differences*

If you do not need an exact difference,
you can estimate.

If a number ends in 5, 6, 7, 8, or 9, you can round up.

If a number ends in 0, 1, 2, 3, or 4, you can round down.

What is 26 − 13?

26 is about the same as 30.

13 is about the same as 10.

30 − 10 = 20, so the exact difference of 26 − 13 will be about 20.

---

## Round each number to the nearest *ten*. Then subtract.

**1.** 59 rounds to _____

12 rounds to _____

59 − 12 is about _____

_____ − _____ = _____

**2.** 28 rounds to _____

19 rounds to _____

28 − 19 is about _____

_____ − _____ = _____

---

**3.** 42 rounds to _____

21 rounds to _____

42 − 21 is about _____

_____ − _____ = _____

**4.** 67 rounds to _____

33 rounds to _____

67 − 33 is about _____

_____ − _____ = _____

Name _____

# Skills Practice

*Estimate Differences*

## Round to the nearest *ten*. Then subtract.
## Use the number lines to help.

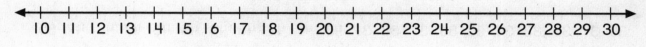

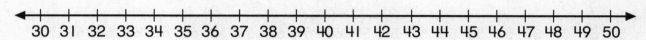

**1.** 39 − 32

    39 rounds to _____

    32 rounds to _____

    _____ − _____ = _____

**2.** 48 − 24

    48 rounds to _____

    24 rounds to _____

    _____ − _____ = _____

**3.** 47 − 28

    _____ − _____ = _____

**4.** 49 − 17

    _____ − _____ = _____

**5.** 38 − 21

    _____ − _____ = _____

**6.** 43 − 14

    _____ − _____ = _____

## Solve.

**7.** Lily has 57 marbles. Her brother has 22 marbles.
About how many more marbles does Lily have?

    _____ − _____ = _____

She has about _____ more marbles.

Name _____

# Chapter Foldables Rubric

| Score | Explanation |
|---|---|
| 3 | Student used 8 pocket Foldables to place the appropriate lessons in the appropriate folders.<br><br>Student successfully added using two-digit numbers and using estimation.<br><br>Student successfully modeled subtraction of two-digit numbers and estimation. |
| 2 | Student used 8 pocket Foldables to place the appropriate lessons in the appropriate folders.<br><br>Student successfully added using two-digit numbers and using a new strategy, estimation. |
| 1 | Student used 8 pocket Foldables to place the appropriate lessons in the appropriate folders.<br><br>Student did not understand the concept of estimation. |
| 0 | Student did not place the correct lessons in their appropriate folder.<br><br>Student did not successfully model two-digit addition and subtraction. |

Assessment

Name _____

# Chapter Test, Form I

**Fill in the circle for the correct answer.**

1.  50
    − 20

   ○ 70
   ○ 30
   ○ 50
   ○ 40

2.  40
   +30

   ○ 70
   ○ 10
   ○ 50
   ○ 60

3.  25
   + 3

   ○ 29
   ○ 22
   ○ 26
   ○ 28

4.  43
   +22

   ○ 21
   ○ 65
   ○ 61
   ○ 68

5.  67
    − 2

   ○ 65
   ○ 59
   ○ 63
   ○ 69

6.  58
   −21

   ○ 76
   ○ 79
   ○ 37
   ○ 35

**GO on**

**Round each number to the nearest *ten*. Then add.
Fill in the circle for the correct answer.**

7.  25
    +21

    ○ about 50
    ○ about 10
    ○ about 45
    ○ about 60

8.  48
    − 26

    ○ about 20
    ○ about 23
    ○ about 80
    ○ about 10

9.

dolls 15

cars 5

planes 10

**Rick has 20 toys. Which two kinds of toys does he have?**
    ○ dolls and planes
    ○ cars and planes
    ○ planes and dolls
    ○ dolls and cars

STOP

**Fill in the circle for the correct answer.**

1. Jen sees 20 things in her yard. Guess which two kinds of things she sees.

ants 12          bees 8          flowers 18

- ○ bees and flowers
- ○ ants and bees
- ○ flowers and bees
- ○ bees and flowers

2. Tim walks 11 blocks. Ann walks 28 blocks. How many more blocks does Ann walk?
- ○ 17
- ○ 15
- ○ 10
- ○ 39

**Round each number to the nearest ten. Then add.**

3.  25
   − 21
   ___
- ○ about 50
- ○ about 10
- ○ about 45
- ○ about 20

**GO on**

Name _____

# Chapter Test, Form 2A *(continued)*

## Fill in the circle for the correct answer.

Copyright © Macmillan/McGraw-Hill, a division of The McGraw-Hill Companies, Inc.

Assessment

5.  42
    + 4    ○ 38        ○ 45
           ○ 41        ○ 46

6.  15
    +43    ○ 55        ○ 53
           ○ 58        ○ 61

7.  70
    −50    ○ 80        ○ 30
           ○ 10        ○ 20

8.  45
    −13    ○ 32        ○ 58
           ○ 31        ○ 37

9.  89
    − 5    ○ 82        ○ 84
           ○ 94        ○ 80

10. 60
    +20    ○ 80        ○ 40
           ○ 90        ○ 70

**STOP**

Name _____

# Chapter Test, Form 2B

## Fill in the circle for the correct answer.

1. $\begin{array}{r} 76 \\ -\phantom{0}3 \\ \hline \end{array}$
   - ◯ 79
   - ◯ 71
   - ◯ 73

2. $\begin{array}{r} 50 \\ +20 \\ \hline \end{array}$
   - ◯ 70
   - ◯ 30
   - ◯ 80

3. $\begin{array}{r} 15 \\ +\phantom{0}4 \\ \hline \end{array}$
   - ◯ 11
   - ◯ 19
   - ◯ 18

4. $\begin{array}{r} 39 \\ -14 \\ \hline \end{array}$
   - ◯ 25
   - ◯ 54
   - ◯ 27

5. $\begin{array}{r} 50 \\ -40 \\ \hline \end{array}$
   - ◯ 90
   - ◯ 20
   - ◯ 10

6. $\begin{array}{r} 37 \\ +22 \\ \hline \end{array}$
   - ◯ 55
   - ◯ 58
   - ◯ 59

**GO on**

**Fill in th circle for the correct answer.**

**7.** Mr. Cobb made 20 pies. He sold 13.
How many are left?

◯ 7

◯ 33

◯ 10

**8.**

circles 5    squares 10    stars 15

Ann draws 25 shapes.
Which two shapes does she draw?

◯ circles and stars

◯ squares and stars

◯ circles and squares

## Round each number to the nearest *ten*. Then add.

**9.**  19
      +11

◯ about 30

◯ about 10

◯ about 20

**STOP**

Assessment

Name _____

# Chapter Test, Form 2C

## Write your answer.

1.
$$\begin{array}{r} 40 \\ -10 \\ \hline \end{array}$$

2.
$$\begin{array}{r} 50 \\ +40 \\ \hline \end{array}$$

3.
$$\begin{array}{r} 43 \\ + 5 \\ \hline \end{array}$$

4.
$$\begin{array}{r} 51 \\ +37 \\ \hline \end{array}$$

5.
$$\begin{array}{r} 69 \\ - 4 \\ \hline \end{array}$$

6.
$$\begin{array}{r} 87 \\ -44 \\ \hline \end{array}$$

**GO on**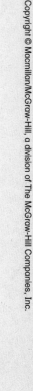

Name _____

# Chapter Test, Form 2C *(continued)*

**Round each number to the nearest *ten*. Write your answer.**

7.    43
    +22
about _____

8.    75
    −34
about _____

## Solve.

9. Leo planted 17 seeds in his yard.
   Which two kinds of seeds did he use?

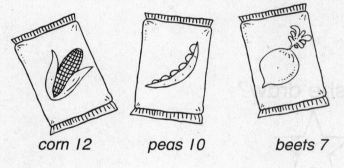

corn 12       peas 10       beets 7

_____

**Put in the missing signs.**

10. 16 ◯ 5 ◯ 4 = 7

STOP

Assessment

# Chapter Test, Form 2D

## Round each number to the nearest *ten*.

**1.**    12
      +29
about _____

**2.**  38
      −16
about _____

**3.**    17
      +42
about _____

**4.**  52
      −22
about _____

## Solve.

**5.** Rose draws 14 shapes.
   Which two shapes does she draw?

circles 4      squares 15      stars 10

_____

GO on

**15**

# Chapter Test, Form 2D *(continued)*

## Write your answer.

6.  $\begin{array}{r} 13 \\ +15 \\ \hline \end{array}$

7.  $\begin{array}{r} 44 \\ -\ 3 \\ \hline \end{array}$

8.  $\begin{array}{r} 50 \\ -40 \\ \hline \end{array}$

9.  $\begin{array}{r} 20 \\ +20 \\ \hline \end{array}$

10.  $\begin{array}{r} 26 \\ +\ 3 \\ \hline \end{array}$

11.  $\begin{array}{r} 38 \\ -15 \\ \hline \end{array}$

STOP

Name _____

# Cumulative Test Practice Chapters 1–15

**Write the correct answer.**
**Add or subtract to solve.**

1.
$$\begin{array}{r} 5 \\ 2 \\ +\ 4 \\ \hline \end{array}$$

2.
$$\begin{array}{r} 10 \\ -10 \\ \hline \end{array}$$

3.
$$\begin{array}{r} 7 \\ -\ 0 \\ \hline \end{array}$$

4.
$$\begin{array}{r} 4 \\ +\ 8 \\ \hline \end{array}$$

5.
$$\begin{array}{r} 5 \\ 5 \\ +\ 1 \\ \hline \end{array}$$

6.
$$\begin{array}{r} 49 \\ -24 \\ \hline \end{array}$$

**Count the coins. Write the value.**

7. = _____ cents

**Count by 5s. Write the numbers.**

8. 5, 10, _____, 20, _____, _____, 35

**Write the numbers in order.**

9. 13, 10, 47, 8, 81, 49

_____, _____, _____, _____, _____, _____

**GO on**

Name _____

# Cumulative Test Practice *(continued)*

Assessment

## Fill in the circle for the correct answer.

**10.** What comes next?

○  ○ ☆

○ 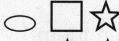 □ ☆

○  ☆ ☆

○  ☆ ○

**11.** What time is it?

○ 12:00

○ 14:30

○ 6:00

○ 12:30

**12.** What is this object called?

○ square

○ sphere

○ cube

○ triangle

STOP

Name _____

# End-of-Year Test

**Circle or write the correct answer on the line.**

1. Circle the pattern unit.

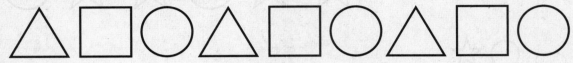

2. 4 friends are playing tag. 5 more friends join them.
   How many friends are playing tag now?
   Write the correct number sentence.

   _____ + _____ = _____ friends

3. Ling and her mom baked 12 muffins. They ate 2 of them.

   How many muffins are there now? _____ muffins

4. Use the tally chart to solve.

| Favorite Art Project | |
|---|---|
| Painting | 卌 |
| Pottery | 卌 ||| |
| Coloring | || |

   How many more students voted for pottery than coloring? _____ students

5. 4 + 4 = _____

6. 9 + 3 = 12. Write the related subtraction facts.

   _____

**GO on**

Assessment

7. Write the numbers that are 2 more and 2 less than 64.

   _____ and _____

8. Circle the ribbon that is longer.

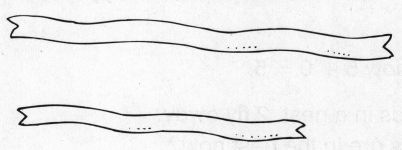

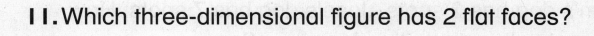

9. Find the missing numbers.

   $13 - 6 =$ _____

   $6 +$ _____ $= 13$

10. A juice box is 50¢. Tom buys one with two coins.

    What coins does Tom use?

    _____

11. Which three-dimensional figure has 2 flat faces?

    _____

12. Write 2 tens and 3 ones another way.

    _____

GO on

Name _____

13. Circle your answer. 15 _____ 10

   is greater than (>)   is less than (<)   is equal to (=)

14.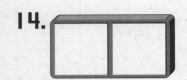

   Draw dots to show $5 + 0 = 5$.

15. There are 5 birds in a nest. 2 fly away.
   How many birds are in the nest now?

   _____ birds

16.

| Favorite Music | | | | | | | |
|---|---|---|---|---|---|---|---|
| Rock | ☺ | ☺ | ☺ | ☺ | ☺ | | | |
| Dance | ☺ | ☺ | ☺ | ☺ | ☺ | ☺ | | |
| Country | ☺ | ☺ | ☺ | | | | | |

   Which music has the most votes? _____

17. Kim's dog has 3 spots. Jose's dog has 7 spots. How
   many total spots do the dogs have?

   _____ + _____ = _____ spots

18. Use the number line to help you solve.

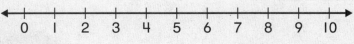

   $8 - 5 =$ _____

GO on

Name _____

## End-of-Year Test *(continued)*

Copyright © Macmillan/McGraw-Hill, a division of The McGraw-Hill Companies, Inc.

Assessment

19. Tim counts by fives. Write the numbers he missed:

   5, 10, _____, 20, _____, 30

20. Circle the one that holds the *most*.

21. Circle the numbers you add first. Then find the sum.

   3 + 5 + 7 = _____

22. Elena buys an orange. She spends 3 nickels and 3 pennies. How much does the orange cost?

   _____¢

23. Chen draws a shape that has no sides. What shape does Chen draw?

   _____

24.    71
      − 5
      ‾‾‾‾

STOP

# Answers (Graphic Organizer & Anticipation Guide)

Name _____

## 15  Anticipation Guide

**Directions:** Before you begin Chapter 15, distribute the Anticipation Guide to students. Read each question to the students, giving them time to answer each question. You may want to ask them the same questions after students complete the chapter.

| Before Chapter | | After Chapter |
|---|---|---|
| | 1. What are the addends in 6 + 5 = 11? | 6 and 5 |
| | 2. What is the sum in 6 + 5 = 11? | 11 |
| | 3. What is the difference in 11 – 6 = 5? | 5 |
| | 4. Which number is in the ones place in 427? | 7 |
| | 5. Which number is in the tens place in 427? | 2 |
| | 6. Round 48 to the nearest 10. | 50 |
| | 7. Is 47 – 28 about 20? | yes |
| ○ ○ | 8. Put in the correct signs.   14 ○ 6   3 = 23 | ⊕ ⊕ |

---

Name _____

## 15  Graphic Organizer
*Two-Column Chart*

A suggestion for how to use this organizer can be found in the answer pages at the back of this book.

10  11  12  13  14  15  16  17  18  19  20  21  22  23  24  25  26  27  28  29  30

| Number | Round to nearest 10 |
|---|---|
| 13 | 10 |
| 21 | 20 |
| 11 | 10 |
| 26 | 30 |
| 19 | 20 |
| 22 | 20 |

**Note to Teacher: This organizer can help students round numbers to the nearest 10. Write numbers from 10–30 in the first column. Have students use the number line to round each number to the nearest 10.**

Answers

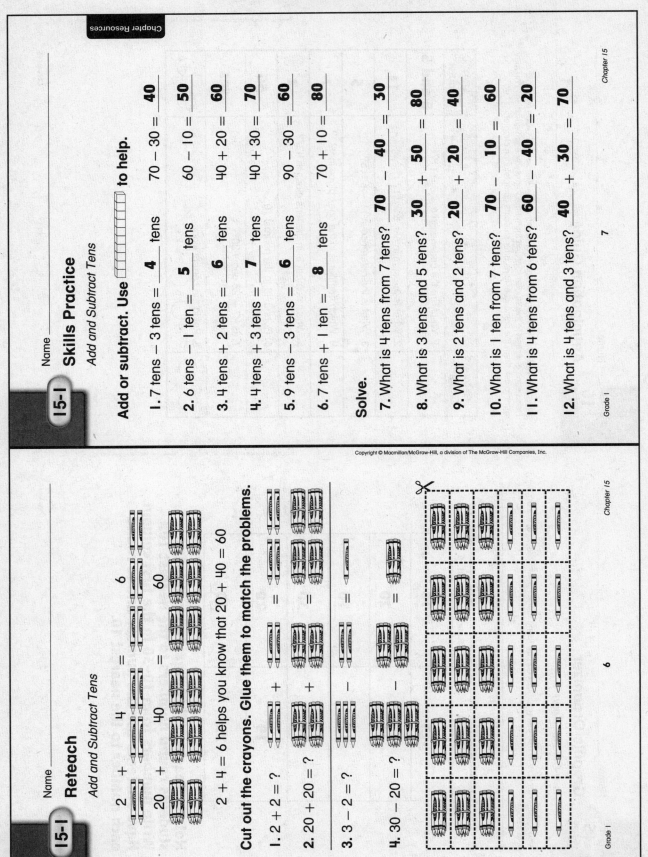

## 15-1 Skills Practice

*Add and Subtract Tens*

Name

**Add or subtract. Use [ten block] to help.**

1. 7 tens – 3 tens = __4__ tens    70 – 30 = __40__
2. 6 tens – 1 ten = __5__ tens    60 – 10 = __50__
3. 4 tens + 2 tens = __6__ tens    40 + 20 = __60__
4. 4 tens + 3 tens = __7__ tens    40 + 30 = __70__
5. 9 tens – 3 tens = __6__ tens    90 – 30 = __60__
6. 7 tens + 1 ten = __8__ tens    70 + 10 = __80__

**Solve.**

7. What is 4 tens from 7 tens? __70__ – __40__ = __30__
8. What is 3 tens and 5 tens? __30__ + __50__ = __80__
9. What is 2 tens and 2 tens? __20__ + __20__ = __40__
10. What is 1 ten from 7 tens? __70__ – __10__ = __60__
11. What is 4 tens from 6 tens? __60__ – __40__ = __20__
12. What is 4 tens and 3 tens? __40__ + __30__ = __70__

Grade 1    7    Chapter 15

## 15-1 Reteach

*Add and Subtract Tens*

Name

2 + 4 = 6

20 + 40 = 60

2 + 4 = 6 helps you know that 20 + 40 = 60

**Cut out the crayons. Glue them to match the problems.**

1. 2 + 2 = ?
2. 20 + 20 = ?
3. 3 – 2 = ?
4. 30 – 20 = ?

Grade 1    6    Chapter 15

Name _____

## 15-1 Problem-Solving Practice
*Add and Subtract Tens*

**Solve. Use ▭ to help.**

1. Lily has 5 tens. She counts back 2 tens. How many are left?

   5 tens − 2 tens = **3** tens     50 − 20 = **30**

2. Tim has 50 crayons. He gets 20 more. How many crayons does he have now?

   **50** + **20** = **70** crayons

3. Jose counts 20 blue bugs, 30 red bugs, and 10 yellow bugs. How many bugs does he count in all?

   **20** (+) **30** (+) **10** = **60** bugs

4. Calvin has 3 tens and 4 tens. How many does he have?

   3 tens + 4 tens = **7** tens     30 + 40 = **70**

5. Flora has 40 apples. She eats 10 of them. How many apples are left?

   40 (−) 10 = **30** apples

---

Name _____

## 15-1 Homework Practice
*Add and Subtract Tens*

**Add or subtract. Use ▭ to help.**

1. 9 tens − 1 tens = **8** tens     90 − 10 = **80**

2. 8 tens + 1 ten = **9** tens     80 + 10 = **90**

3. 6 tens − 1 ten = **5** tens     60 − 10 = **50**

4. 3 tens + 3 tens = **6** tens     30 + 30 = **60**

5. 8 tens − 3 tens = **5** tens     80 − 30 = **50**

6. 5 tens + 1 ten = **6** tens     50 + 10 = **60**

**Solve.**

7. What is 2 tens from 7 tens?   **70** − **20** = **50**

8. What is 6 tens and 2 tens?   **60** + **20** = **80**

9. What is 3 tens from 5 tens?   **50** − **30** = **20**

10. What is 1 ten from 6 tens?   **60** − **10** = **50**

11. What is 1 ten and 6 tens?   **10** + **60** = **70**

12. What is 2 tens and 3 tens?   **20** + **30** = **50**

Answers

# Answers (Lessons 15-1 and 15-2)

Name _____

## 15-2 Reteach

*Add with Two-Digit Numbers*

**You can count on a number line to add with two-digit numbers.**

Mary buys 32 eggs.
Jen buys 5 more eggs than Mary.
How many eggs did Jen buy?

$32 + 5 = ?$

30  31  32  33  34  35  36  **37**  38  39  40

$32 + 5 = 37$ eggs

**Use the number line to add.**

1.
10  11  12  13  14  15  16  17  18  19  20
$14 + 3 =$ **17**
$18 + 2 =$ **20**

2.
20  21  22  23  24  25  26  27  28  29  30
$21 + 4 =$ **25**
$24 + 3 =$ **27**

3.
30  31  32  33  34  35  36  37  38  39  40
$36 + 3 =$ **39**
$31 + 5 =$ **36**

4.
60  61  62  63  64  65  66  67  68  69  70
$63 + 5 =$ **68**
$65 + 3 =$ **68**

Name _____

## 15-1 Enrich

*Add and Subtract Tens*

**Read each riddle.**
**Write the answer.**

1. If you subtract 30 from my number, the answer is 60. What number am I?

   I am **90**.

2. Subtract 2 tens from 80. What number do you have?

   You have **60**.

3. If you add 10 to my number, the answer is 50. What number am I?

   I am **40**.

4. If you subtract 10 from my number, the answer is 40. What number am I?

   I am **50**.

5. If you subtract 30 from my number, the answer is 40. What number am I?

   I am **70**.

6. What number do you have if you add 1 ten to 80?

   You have **90**.

7. What number do you have if you subtract 2 tens from 90?

   You have **70**.

8. If you add 20 to my number, the answer is 70. What number am I?

   I am **50**.

# Answers (Lesson 15-2)

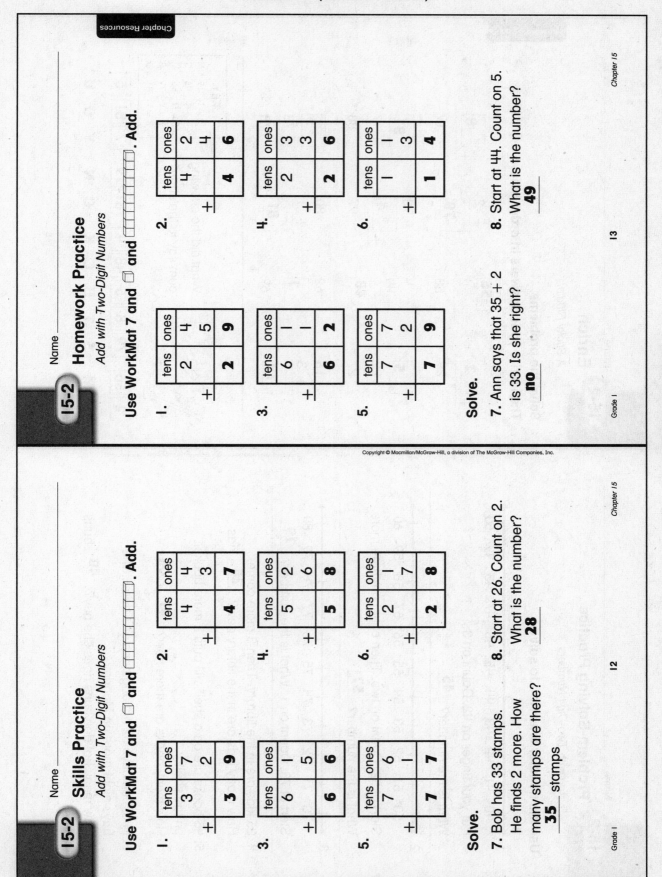

Chapter Resources

Name _____

## 15-2 Homework Practice
### Add with Two-Digit Numbers

Use WorkMat 7 and ▯ and ▭. Add.

1.

| | tens | ones |
|---|---|---|
| | 2 | 4 |
| + | | 5 |
| | **2** | **9** |

2.

| | tens | ones |
|---|---|---|
| | 4 | 2 |
| + | | 4 |
| | **4** | **6** |

3.

| | tens | ones |
|---|---|---|
| | 6 | — |
| + | | — |
| | **6** | **2** |

4.

| | tens | ones |
|---|---|---|
| | 2 | 3 |
| + | | 3 |
| | **2** | **6** |

5.

| | tens | ones |
|---|---|---|
| | 7 | 7 |
| + | | 2 |
| | **7** | **9** |

6.

| | tens | ones |
|---|---|---|
| | — | — |
| + | | 3 |
| | **1** | **4** |

Solve.

7. Ann says that 35 + 2 is 33. Is she right? **no**

8. Start at 44. Count on 5. What is the number? **49**

Name _____

## 15-2 Skills Practice
### Add with Two-Digit Numbers

Use WorkMat 7 and ▯ and ▭. Add.

1.

| | tens | ones |
|---|---|---|
| | 3 | 7 |
| + | | 2 |
| | **3** | **9** |

2.

| | tens | ones |
|---|---|---|
| | 4 | 4 |
| + | | 3 |
| | **4** | **7** |

3.

| | tens | ones |
|---|---|---|
| | 6 | — |
| + | | 5 |
| | **6** | **6** |

4.

| | tens | ones |
|---|---|---|
| | 5 | 2 |
| + | | 6 |
| | **5** | **8** |

5.

| | tens | ones |
|---|---|---|
| | 7 | 6 |
| + | | — |
| | **7** | **7** |

6.

| | tens | ones |
|---|---|---|
| | 2 | — |
| + | | 7 |
| | **2** | **8** |

Solve.

7. Bob has 33 stamps. He finds 2 more. How many stamps are there? **35** stamps

8. Start at 26. Count on 2. What is the number? **28**

Answers

# Answers (Lesson 15-2)

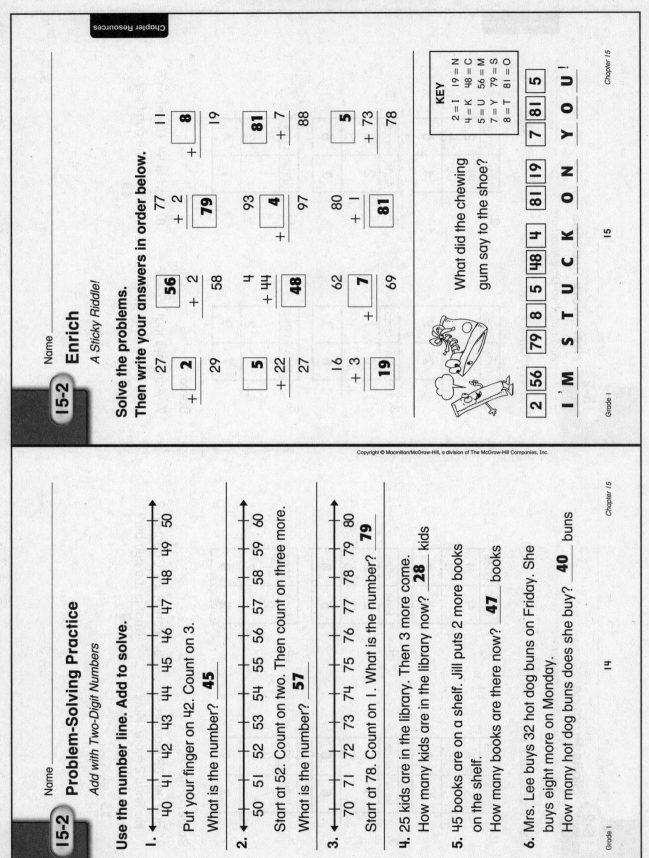

**15-2**

Name _____

## Enrich
*A Sticky Riddle!*

**Solve the problems.**
**Then write your answers in order below.**

```
    27        56        77
  +  2      +  2      +  2
    29        58        79
```

```
     5         4        93
  + 22      + 44       + 4
    27        48        97
```

```
    16        62        80
  +  3      +  7      +  1
    19        69        81
```

```
     8
  + 11
    19
```

```
    81
  +  7
    88
```

```
     5
  + 73
    78
```

What did the chewing
gum say to the shoe?

| KEY | |
|---|---|
| 2 = I | 19 = N |
| 4 = K | 48 = C |
| 5 = U | 56 = M |
| 7 = Y | 79 = S |
| 8 = T | 81 = O |

| 2 | 56 | 79 | 8 | 5 | 48 | 4 | 81 | 19 | 7 | 81 | 5 |
|---|---|---|---|---|---|---|---|---|---|---|---|
| I' | M | S | T | U | C | K | O | N | Y | O | U |

I' M   S T U C K   O N   Y O U !

Grade 1          15          *Chapter 15*

---

**15-2**

Name _____

## Problem-Solving Practice
*Add with Two-Digit Numbers*

**Use the number line. Add to solve.**

1. ⟵ 40  41  42  43  44  45  46  47  48  49  50 ⟶

   Put your finger on 42. Count on 3.
   What is the number? __45__

2. ⟵ 50  51  52  53  54  55  56  57  58  59  60 ⟶

   Start at 52. Count on two. Then count on three more.
   What is the number? __57__

3. ⟵ 70  71  72  73  74  75  76  77  78  79  80 ⟶

   Start at 78. Count on 1. What is the number? __79__

4. 25 kids are in the library. Then 3 more come.
   How many kids are in the library now? __28__ kids

5. 45 books are on a shelf. Jill puts 2 more books
   on the shelf.
   How many books are there now? __47__ books

6. Mrs. Lee buys 32 hot dog buns on Friday. She
   buys eight more on Monday.
   How many hot dog buns does she buy? __40__ buns

Grade 1          14          *Chapter 15*

# Answers (Lesson 15-3)

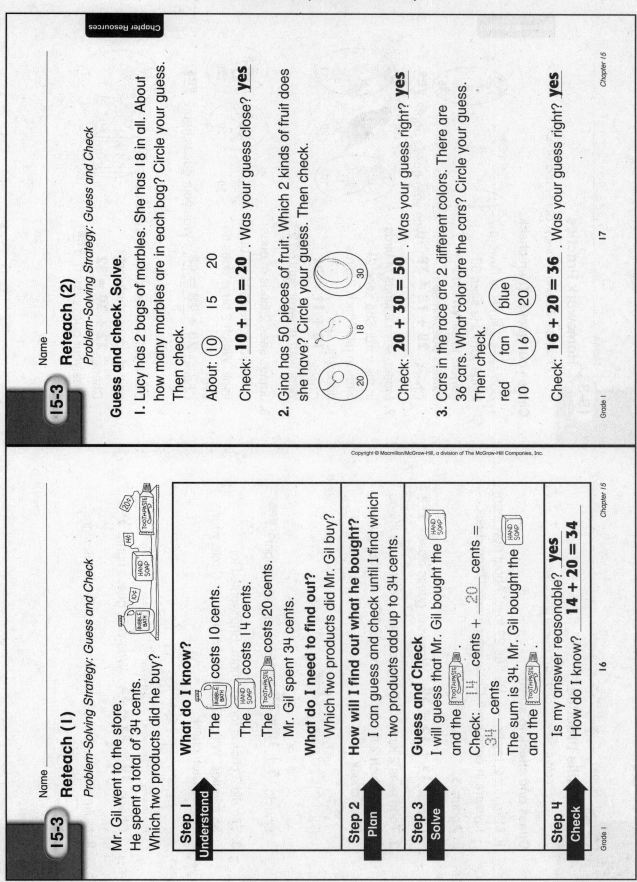

Name _____

## 15-3 Reteach (2)

*Problem-Solving Strategy: Guess and Check*

**Guess and check. Solve.**

1. Lucy has 2 bags of marbles. She has 18 in all. About how many marbles are in each bag? Circle your guess. Then check.

About:  (10)   15   20

Check: **10 + 10 = 20** . Was your guess close? **yes**

2. Gina has 50 pieces of fruit. Which 2 kinds of fruit does she have? Circle your guess. Then check.

30   18   20

Check: **20 + 30 = 50** . Was your guess right? **yes**

3. Cars in the race are 2 different colors. There are 36 cars. What color are the cars? Circle your guess. Then check.

red   tan   blue
10    16   (20)

Check: **16 + 20 = 36** . Was your guess right? **yes**

---

Name _____

## 15-3 Reteach (1)

*Problem-Solving Strategy: Guess and Check*

Mr. Gil went to the store.
He spent a total of 34 cents.
Which two products did he buy?

**Step 1 Understand**

**What do I know?**

The [BUBBLE BATH] costs 10 cents.

The [HAND SOAP] costs 14 cents.

The [TOOTHPASTE] costs 20 cents.

Mr. Gil spent 34 cents.

**What do I need to find out?**

Which two products did Mr. Gil buy?

**Step 2 Plan**

**How will I find out what he bought?**

I can guess and check until I find which two products add up to 34 cents.

**Step 3 Solve**

**Guess and Check**

I will guess that Mr. Gil bought the [TOOTHPASTE] and the [HAND SOAP].

Check: __14__ cents + __20__ cents = __34__ cents

The sum is 34. Mr. Gil bought the [TOOTHPASTE] and the [HAND SOAP].

**Step 4 Check**

Is my answer reasonable? **yes**
How do I know? **14 + 20 = 34**

## 15-3

Name _____

## Homework Practice

*Problem-Solving Strategy: Guess and Check*

**Circle your guess. Then check.**

1. Bob sees 2 kinds of flowers in the yard. He sees 38 flowers in all. Which 2 flowers does he see?

Check: **20 + 18 = 38** . Was your guess right? **yes**

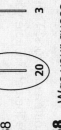

20    3    18

2. Marlee sees 2 kinds of birds in the yard. She sees 21 birds in all. Which 2 birds does she see?

Check: **10 + 11 = 21** .
Was your answer right? **yes**

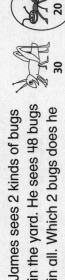

10    20    11

3. James sees 2 kinds of bugs in the yard. He sees 48 bugs in all. Which 2 bugs does he see?

Check: **20 + 28 = 48** . Was your guess right? **yes**

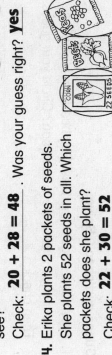

30    20    28

4. Erika plants 2 packets of seeds. She plants 52 seeds in all. Which packets does she plant?

Check: **22 + 30 = 52** .
Was your guess right? **yes**

22    20    30

Grade 1    19    *Chapter 15*

## 15-3

Name _____

## Skills Practice

*Problem-Solving Strategy: Guess and Check*

**Guess and check to solve.**

1. Mike has 2 toy boxes. He has 29 toys. About how many toys are in each box? Circle your guess. Then check.

About:   5    10    (15)

Check: **15 + 15 = 30** . Was your guess close? **yes**

2. Todd sees 2 kinds of things outside. He sees 15 things in all. Which 2 things does he see? Circle your guess. Then check.

5    7    10

Check: **5 + 10 = 15** . Was your guess right? **yes**

3. Ella did 2 chores for her mom. She worked for 35 minutes. Which 2 chores did she do? Circle your guess. Then check.

10 minutes    15 minutes    25 minutes    30 minutes

Check: **10 + 25 = 35** . Was your guess right? **yes**

4. Make this number sentence correct. Put in the signs.

32  $-$  25  $-$  7 = 0

Grade 1    18    *Chapter 15*

# Answers (Lessons 15-3 and 15-4)

## 15-4 Reteach

Name _____

**Add Two-Digit Numbers**

You can use a number line to add ones or tens.

Lu plants 23 flowers. Meg plants 35 flowers.
How many flowers are there now?

$23 + 35 = ?$

**Count on by ones to add one.**
**Start with the greater number.**

$5 + 3 = 8$ ones

**Count on by tens to add ten.**
**Start with the greater number.**

$30 + 20 = 50$

50 tens and 8 ones = 58 flowers

**Use the number lines to add ones and tens.**

1. $42 + 24 =$ **66**
2. $78 + 11 =$ **89**
3. $31 + 52 =$ **83**
4. $15 + 14 =$ **29**

Grade 1 ..... 21 ..... Chapter 15

## 15-3 Enrich

Name _____

**Add It Up**

Use the shapes to add. Write the addition sentence and solve.

1. $11 + 3 = 14$
2. $12 + 5 = 17$
3. $13 + 6 = 19$
4. $14 + 3 = 17$
5. $15 + 1 = 16$

Grade 1 ..... 20 ..... Chapter 15

Grade 1 ..... A9 ..... Chapter 15

**Answers**

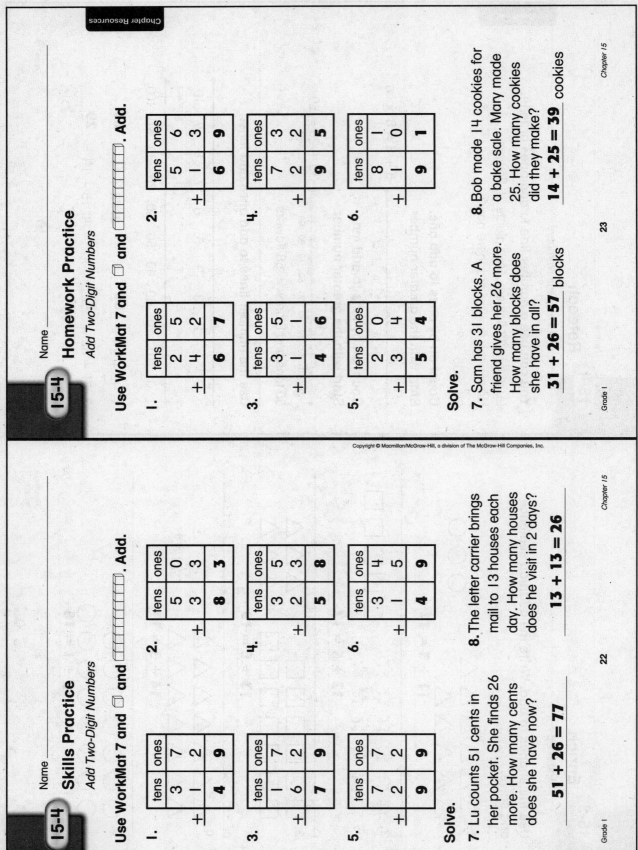

**Homework Practice**

Name _____

**15-4**

## Homework Practice
*Add Two-Digit Numbers*

Use WorkMat 7 and ▢ and ▭. Add.

1.
| tens | ones |
|---|---|
| 2 | 5 |
| + 4 | 2 |
| **6** | **7** |

2.
| tens | ones |
|---|---|
| 5 | 6 |
| + 1 | 3 |
| **6** | **9** |

3.
| tens | ones |
|---|---|
| 3 | 5 |
| + 1 | 1 |
| **4** | **6** |

4.
| tens | ones |
|---|---|
| 7 | 3 |
| + 2 | 2 |
| **9** | **5** |

5.
| tens | ones |
|---|---|
| 2 | 0 |
| + 3 | 4 |
| **5** | **4** |

6.
| tens | ones |
|---|---|
| 8 | 1 |
| + 1 | 0 |
| **9** | **1** |

Solve.

7. Sam has 31 blocks. A friend gives her 26 more. How many blocks does she have in all?

$31 + 26 = $ **57** blocks

8. Bob made 14 cookies for a bake sale. Mary made 25. How many cookies did they make?

$14 + 25 = $ **39** cookies

---

**Skills Practice**

Name _____

**15-4**

## Skills Practice
*Add Two-Digit Numbers*

Use WorkMat 7 and ▢ and ▭. Add.

1.
| tens | ones |
|---|---|
| 3 | 7 |
| + 1 | 2 |
| **4** | **9** |

2.
| tens | ones |
|---|---|
| 5 | 0 |
| + 3 | 3 |
| **8** | **3** |

3.
| tens | ones |
|---|---|
| 1 | 7 |
| + 6 | 2 |
| **7** | **9** |

4.
| tens | ones |
|---|---|
| 3 | 5 |
| + 2 | 3 |
| **5** | **8** |

5.
| tens | ones |
|---|---|
| 7 | 7 |
| + 2 | 2 |
| **9** | **9** |

6.
| tens | ones |
|---|---|
| 3 | 4 |
| + 1 | 5 |
| **4** | **9** |

Solve.

7. Lu counts 51 cents in her pocket. She finds 26 more. How many cents does she have now?

$51 + 26 = $ **77**

8. The letter carrier brings mail to 13 houses each day. How many houses does he visit in 2 days?

$13 + 13 = $ **26**

Chapter Resources

Name _____

## 15-4 Enrich

*Get Well Greetings*

**Ms. Reed's first grade class is making cards for people in the local hospital. Use the clues to find out how many cards are made.**

1. Tara uses glitter to make 24 cards. Seth uses the computer to make his cards. He makes 21 more cards than Tara makes.

   How many cards does Seth make?

   **24** + **21** = **45** cards

2. Cole paints 12 cards. Tom uses markers to make 27 cards.

   How many cards do they make together?

   **12** + **27** = **39** cards

3. Kim and Mae both use colored pencils to make a total of 50 cards. If Kim makes 29 cards,

   how many does Mae make?

   29 + **21** = **50** cards

4. Brady uses markers to draw his cards. Mia uses stamps to make her 32 cards. If Brady and Mia make 49 cards together,

   how many cards does Brady make?

   32 + **17** = **49** cards

Grade 1     25     Chapter 15

---

Name _____

## 15-4 Problem-Solving Practice

*Add Two-Digit Numbers*

**Solve.**

1. Mac walks 12 blocks to school. Jody walks 14 blocks. How many blocks do they walk in all?

   **12** + **14** = **26** blocks

2. Raul has 21 toy cars. He gets a set of 35 cars for his birthday. How many cars does he have now?

   **21** + **35** = **56** cars

3. 44 frogs, 21 fish, and 23 bugs live in a pond. How many bugs and frogs are there?

   **23 + 44 = 67** bugs and frogs

4. One farm has 21 pigs. The other farm has 44 pigs. How many pigs are there in all?

   **21** + **44** = **65** pigs

5. Rosa finds 36 ants outside. She finds 11 more in the shed. How many ants does she find?

   **36 + 11 = 47** ants

6. Leo has 13 red crayons, 24 blue crayons, and 45 yellow crayons. How many blue and yellow crayons does Leo have?

   **24 + 45 = 69** blue and yellow crayons

Grade 1     24     Chapter 15

Answers

# Answers (Lesson 15-5)

## 15-5 Reteach
*Estimate Sums*

Name _____

If you do not need an exact sum, you can estimate.
If a number ends in 0, 1, 2, 3, or 4, you can round down.
If a number ends in 5, 6, 7, 8, or 9, you can round up.

What is 33 + 19?

33 is about the same as 30.

19 is about the same as 20.

30 + 20 = 50, so the exact sum of 33 + 19 will be about 50.

**Round each number to the nearest ten. Then add.**

1. 59 rounds to **60**    32 rounds to **30**
   59 + 32 is about **90**    **60** + **30** = **90**

2. 44 rounds to **40**    13 rounds to **10**
   44 + 13 is about **50**    **40** + **10** = **50**

3. 38 rounds to **40**    21 rounds to **20**
   38 + 21 is about **60**    **40** + **20** = **60**

4. 41 rounds to **40**    43 rounds to **40**
   41 + 43 is about **80**    **40** + **40** = **80**

## 15-5 Skills Practice
*Estimate Sums*

Name _____

**Round to the nearest *ten*. Then add.**
**Use the number lines to help.**

10 11 12 13 14 15 16 17 18 19 20 21 22 23 24 25 26 27 28 29 30

30 31 32 33 34 35 36 37 38 39 40 41 42 43 44 45 46 47 48 49 50

1. 47 + 29
   47 rounds to **50**
   29 rounds to **30**
   **50** + **30** = **80**

2. 22 + 13
   22 rounds to **20**
   13 rounds to **10**
   **20** + **10** = **30**

3. 24 + 28
   **20** + **30** = **50**

4. 39 + 17
   **40** + **20** = **60**

5. 33 + 11
   **30** + **10** = **40**

6. 31 + 42
   **30** + **40** = **70**

**Solve.**

7. Lee had 21 stickers. She gets 11 more. About how many does she have now?
   **20** + **10** = **30**    She has about **30** stickers.

8. Tom had 62 marbles. His sister gives him 25 more. About how many marbles does he have now?
   **60** + **30** = **90**    He has about **90** marbles.

# Answers (Lesson 15-5)

**15-5**

Name _____

## Problem-Solving Practice
*Estimate Sums*

**Estimate to solve.**

1. Mr. Smith has 11 cents. Mrs. Smith has 19 cents. About how much do they have?

   **10** + **20** = **30**   They have about **30** cents.

2. Mike's dad got 29 letters this week. He got 21 letters last week. About how many letters did he get?

   **30** + **20** = **50**   He got about **50** letters.

3. Ella found 9 acorns in the yard. She found 27 acorns at the park. She says she has about 30 acorns.

   Is she right? **No**   How do you know? **10 + 30 = 40**

4. Mike has 9 cents. Rita has 31 cents. About how much do they have?

   **10** + **30** = **40**   They have about **40** cents.

5. Suzie looked at the pictures in 24 books last month. She looked at 19 books this month. About how many books has she looked at?

   **20** + **20** = **40**

   She looked at about **40** books.

---

**15-5**

Name _____

## Homework Practice
*Estimate Sums*

**Round to the nearest *ten*. Then add. Use the number lines to help.**

10 11 12 13 14 15 16 17 18 19 20 21 22 23 24 25 26 27 28 29 30

30 31 32 33 34 35 36 37 38 39 40 41 42 43 44 45 46 47 48 49 50

1. 33 + 19

   33 rounds to **30**

   19 rounds to **20**

   **30** + **20** = **50**

2. 41 + 41

   41 rounds to **40**

   41 rounds to **40**

   **40** + **40** = **80**

3. 34 + 18

   **30** + **20** = **50**

4. 26 + 34

   **30** + **30** = **60**

5. 23 + 47

   **20** + **50** = **70**

6. 28 + 19

   **30** + **20** = **50**

**Solve.**

7. Mark has 18 cents. He finds 33 more in his desk. About how much does he have now?

   **20** + **30** = **50**   He has about **50** cents.

8. Chef's mom gives him 16 pennies. His dad gives him 19. Chet says he has about 40 pennies.

   Is he right? **Yes**   How do you know? **20 + 20 = 40**

**Answers**

# Answers (Lessons 15-5 and 15-6)

## 15-6

**Name** _____

### Reteach
*Subtract with Two-Digit Numbers*

You can count back on a number line to subtract from two-digit numbers.

Larry has 28 stamps. He uses 5 of them.
How many stamps are left?

$28 - 5 = ?$

Start at the greater number and count back.

20  21  22  **23**  24  25  26  27  28  29  30

$28 - 5 = 23$ stamps

**Use the number line to subtract.**

10 11 12 13 14 15 16 17 18 19 20

1. $\begin{array}{r} 15 \\ -\ 4 \\ \hline \textbf{11} \end{array}$

20 21 22 23 24 25 26 27 28 29 30

2. $\begin{array}{r} 29 \\ -\ 2 \\ \hline \textbf{27} \end{array}$

30 31 32 33 34 35 36 37 38 39 40

3. $\begin{array}{r} 38 \\ -\ 6 \\ \hline \textbf{32} \end{array}$

50 51 52 53 54 55 56 57 58 59 60

4. $\begin{array}{r} 57 \\ -\ 7 \\ \hline \textbf{50} \end{array}$

Grade 1          31          Chapter 15

---

## 15-5

**Name** _____

### Enrich
*A Cheesy Situation*

Help Moe the mouse get each piece of cheese
to its mouse hole. Round to solve the problems.
Draw a line to the correct sum.

90   80   40   60   70

$\begin{array}{r} 46 \\ +21 \\ \hline \end{array}$   $\begin{array}{r} 76 \\ +12 \\ \hline \end{array}$   $\begin{array}{r} 32 \\ +34 \\ \hline \end{array}$   $\begin{array}{r} 42 \\ +36 \\ \hline \end{array}$   $\begin{array}{r} 13 \\ +33 \\ \hline \end{array}$

Grade 1          30          Chapter 15

# Answers (Lesson 15-6)

## 15-6 Skills Practice

### Subtract with Two-Digit Numbers

**Use WorkMat 7 and 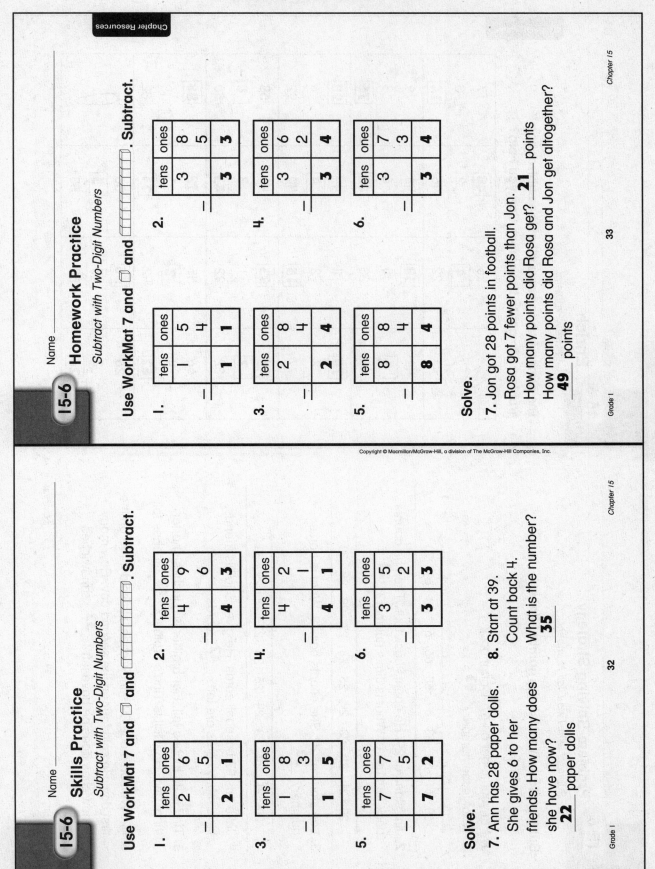. Subtract.**

1.

| tens | ones |
|------|------|
| 2 | 6 |
| − | 5 |
| **2** | **1** |

2.

| tens | ones |
|------|------|
| 4 | 9 |
| − | 6 |
| **4** | **3** |

3.

| tens | ones |
|------|------|
| 1 | 8 |
| − | 3 |
| **1** | **5** |

4.

| tens | ones |
|------|------|
| 4 | 2 |
| − | 1 |
| **4** | **1** |

5.

| tens | ones |
|------|------|
| 7 | 7 |
| − | 5 |
| **7** | **2** |

6.

| tens | ones |
|------|------|
| 3 | 5 |
| − | 2 |
| **3** | **3** |

**Solve.**

7. Ann has 28 paper dolls. She gives 6 to her friends. How many does she have now? **22** paper dolls

8. Start at 39. Count back 4. What is the number? **35**

## 15-6 Homework Practice

### Subtract with Two-Digit Numbers

**Use WorkMat 7 and ☐ and ⬜. Subtract.**

1.

| tens | ones |
|------|------|
| 1 | 5 |
| − | 4 |
| **1** | **1** |

2.

| tens | ones |
|------|------|
| 3 | 8 |
| − | 5 |
| **3** | **3** |

3.

| tens | ones |
|------|------|
| 2 | 8 |
| − | 4 |
| **2** | **4** |

4.

| tens | ones |
|------|------|
| 3 | 6 |
| − | 2 |
| **3** | **4** |

5.

| tens | ones |
|------|------|
| 8 | 8 |
| − | 4 |
| **8** | **4** |

6.

| tens | ones |
|------|------|
| 3 | 7 |
| − | 3 |
| **3** | **4** |

**Solve.**

7. Jon got 28 points in football. Rosa got 7 fewer points than Jon. How many points did Rosa get? **21** points
How many points did Rosa and Jon get altogether? **49** points

**Answers**

## 15-6 Enrich

### A Harey Problem!

**The bunny has to solve all of the subtraction problems to get to the carrot. Can you help?**

| | | | |
|---|---|---|---|
| (rabbit) | $26 - [4] = 22$ | $[48] - 2 = 46$ | $17 - 3 = [14]$ |
| $49 - [4] = 45$ | $[38] - 5 = 33$ | $48 - 6 = [42]$ | $79 - 3 = [76]$ |
| $[79] - 2 = 77$ | $18 - 3 = [15]$ | $44 - [4] = 40$ | $[98] - 6 = 92$ |
| $34 - [2] = 32$ | $[93] - 1 = 92$ | $46 - 3 = [43]$ | $58 - [8] = 50$ |
| $66 - 4 = [62]$ | $45 - [3] = 42$ | $72 - 1 = [71]$ | $[88] - 6 = 82$ |
| $26 - 2 = [24]$ | $[56] - 4 = 52$ | $58 - [5] = 53$ | (carrot) |

Grade 1    35    Chapter 15

---

## 15-6 Problem-Solving Strategy

*Subtract with Two-Digit Numbers*

**Subtract to solve. Use the number lines.**

1. Put your finger on 67. Count back 4. What is the number? __63__

   60 61 62 63 64 65 66 67 68 69 70

2. Jim starts at 29. He counts back four. Then he counts back four more. What is Jim's number? __21__

   20 21 22 23 24 25 26 27 28 29 30

3. Lori starts at 24. She counts back 2. What is Lori's number? __22__

   20 21 22 23 24 25 26 27 28 29 30

4. Jake has 47 baseball cards. He gives 5 to his friends. How many cards are left? __42__ cards

5. Tina is 48 inches tall. Her brother is 6 inches shorter than Tina. How tall is Tina's brother? __42__ inches tall

6. Mr. Watson made 39 sandwiches. He sold three on the first day. He sold four on the second day. How many sandwiches does he have left? __32__ sandwiches

Grade 1    34    Chapter 15

# Answers (Lesson 15-7)

Name _____

## 15-7 Reteach

*Subtract Two-Digit Numbers*

68 birds are in a tree. 47 fly away.
How many birds stay in the tree?

$68 - 47 = ?$

**Count back by ones to subtract one.**

0 1 2 3 4 5 6 7 8 9 10

$8 - 7 = 1$

**Count back by tens to subtract ten.**

0 10 20 30 40 50 60 70 80 90 100

20 and 1 = 21 birds

$60 - 40 = 20$

**Use the number lines to subtract tens and ones.**

0 1 2 3 4 5 6 7 8 9 10

0 10 20 30 40 50 60 70 80 90 100

1. $78 - 17 = $ **61**

2. $38 - 15 = $ **23**

3. $49 - 19 = $ **30**

4. $76 - 33 = $ **43**

5. $57 - 22 = $ **35**

6. $65 - 21 = $ **44**

Grade 1   36   Chapter 15

---

Name _____

## 15-7 Skills Practice

*Subtract Two-Digit Numbers*

**Use WorkMat 7 and ▨ and ▥▥▥ . Subtract.**

1.
| tens | ones |
|------|------|
| 5 | 7 |
| − 1 | 5 |
| **4** | **2** |

2.
| tens | ones |
|------|------|
| 3 | 9 |
| − 2 | 3 |
| **1** | **6** |

3.
| tens | ones |
|------|------|
| 4 | 7 |
| − 3 | 4 |
| **1** | **3** |

4.
| tens | ones |
|------|------|
| 6 | 4 |
| − 3 | 1 |
| **3** | **3** |

5.
| tens | ones |
|------|------|
| 8 | 3 |
| − 1 | 1 |
| **7** | **2** |

6.
| tens | ones |
|------|------|
| 9 | 5 |
| − 1 | 3 |
| **8** | **2** |

**Solve.**

7. Jeff bought 38 cherries. He gave 23 to his dad. How many cherries are left?
**15** cherries

8. Marge counted 59 leaves on a tree. She counts 31 the next day. How many leaves fell off the tree?
**28** leaves

Grade 1   37   Chapter 15

**Answers**

## 15-7

Name _____

## Problem-Solving Practice
*Subtract Two-Digit Numbers*

**Subtract to solve.**

1. Tia is 49 inches tall. Her brother is 35 inches tall.
   How much taller is Tia?
   $$49 - 35 = \underline{14}$$
   Tia is __14__ inches taller than her brother.

2. Jill has 56 coins. She loses 22 of them.
   How many coins are left? __34__ coins

3. 63 crows sit on a fence. 30 fly away. Then 21 more fly away. How many crows are still on the fence? __12__

4. Paco runs for 39 minutes. His sister runs for 11 minutes. How many more minutes does Paco run?
   $$39 - 11 = \underline{28}$$
   Paco runs for __28__ more minutes than his sister.

5. A library has 67 books. 42 books are checked out.
   How many books are left? __25__ books

6. Ms. May has 88 cents. She gives 13 cents to her son. She gives 25 cents to her daughter. How much does Ms. May have left? __50__ cents

---

## 15-7

Name _____

## Homework Practice
*Subtract Two-Digit Numbers*

**Use WorkMat 7 and ☐ and ▭. Subtract.**

1.
| tens | ones |
|------|------|
| 4 | 7 |
| − 2 | 3 |
| **2** | **4** |

2.
| tens | ones |
|------|------|
| 2 | 9 |
| − 1 | 2 |
| **1** | **7** |

3.
| tens | ones |
|------|------|
| 4 | 2 |
| − 1 | 1 |
| **3** | **1** |

4.
| tens | ones |
|------|------|
| 7 | 8 |
| − 5 | 5 |
| **2** | **3** |

5.
| tens | ones |
|------|------|
| 6 | 6 |
| − 5 | 3 |
| **1** | **3** |

6.
| tens | ones |
|------|------|
| 2 | 7 |
| − 1 | 6 |
| **1** | **1** |

**Solve.**

7. Eva found 57 pennies. She keeps 25. How many pennies does she give away?
   __32__ pennies

8. Rick picked 59 apples. He sells 36. How many apples are left?
   __23__ apples

# Answers (Lessons 15-7 and 15-8)

Name _____

## 15-8 Reteach (I)

*Problem-Solving Investigation: Choose a Strategy*

There are 54 dogs and 32 cats at the pet store.
How many more dogs are in the store than cats?

**Step 1 Understand**

**What do I know?**
There are 54 dogs.
There are 32 cats.

**What do I need to find out?**
How many more dogs are there than cats?

**Step 2 Plan**

**How will I find out?**
I can guess and check. But I may not guess the answer right away.
Making a table might be easier.
I will make a table.

**Step 3 Solve**

Make a table.

| Pets | Tens | Ones |
|------|------|------|
| Dogs | 50 | 4 |
| Cats | 30 | 2 |

There are __22__ more dogs than cats.

**Step 4 Check**

Does my table show how many more dogs there are? __yes__

Did I choose a good strategy? __yes__

Chapter 15    41    Grade 1

---

Name _____

## 15-7 Enrich

*Domino Subtraction*

Play a game of Domino Subtraction.
Put your ⚀ facedown.
Turn over 1 ⚀.
Make a subtraction sentence subtracting the little number from the big number.
Add to check.

$$\begin{array}{r} 6 \\ -4 \\ \hline 2 \end{array} \qquad \begin{array}{r} 4 \\ +2 \\ \hline 6 \end{array}$$

**Answers will vary depending on the dominoes chosen.**

1. ☐ ☐ − ☐    ☐ ☐ + ☐

2. ☐ ☐ − ☐    ☐ ☐ + ☐

3. ☐ ☐ − ☐    ☐ ☐ + ☐

4. ☐ ☐ − ☐    ☐ ☐ + ☐

5. ☐ ☐ − ☐    ☐ ☐ + ☐

6. ☐ ☐ − ☐    ☐ ☐ + ☐

Grade 1    40    Chapter 15

## 15-8

Name _____

## Skills Practice

*Problem-Solving Investigation: Choose a Strategy*

**Choose a strategy and solve.**

**Problem Solving Strategies**
- Guess and check
- Choose the operation
- Make a table

1. Lin plants 12 seeds. Dee plants 34 seeds. How many seeds do they plant?

   __46__ seeds

2. Raul has 10 toy cars. He gets a set of 30 cars for his birthday. How many cars does he have now? __40__ cars

3. Lita sees two kinds of objects on her trip. She sees 39 in all. Which two objects does she see? Circle your answer.

   15   18   21

4. The letter carrier brings mail to 20 homes on Lee Street. He brings mail to 10 homes on Main Street. How many homes is that?

   __30__ homes

5. Jen's block has 48 trees. Sam's block has 23 trees. How many more trees are on Jen's block?

   __25__ trees

6. Lou has 16 shirts. Greg has 11 shirts. About how many shirts do they have? Round to the nearest ten.

   About __30__ shirts

43

---

## 15-8

Name _____

## Reteach (2)

*Problem-Solving Investigation: Choose a Strategy*

**Choose a strategy and solve.**

**Problem Solving Strategies**
- Guess and check
- Choose the operation
- Make a table

1. Frank rakes 10 yards. Mike rakes 5. How many yards do they rake in all?

   __15__ yards

2. Stan rides his bike for 32 yards. Lee rides her bike for 56 yards. How many more yards does Lee ride than Stan?

   __24__ yards

3. James sees 2 kinds of flowers in his yard. He sees 40 in all. Which 2 flowers does he see? Circle your answer.

   31   9   20

4. Meg gives 20 cents to her brother. She gives 34 cents to her sister. She has 11 cents left. How much money does she start with?

   __65__ cents

42

---

Chapter Resources

Name _____

15-8

## Enrich

*Subtraction Stories*

**Read the story. Draw a picture. Write a subtraction sentence to solve.**

1. There are 11 bones and 3 dogs. How many more bones are there than dogs?

$$11 - 3 = 8$$

2. There are 12 balloons. 6 balloons pop. How many balloons are left?

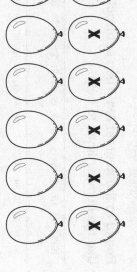

$$12 - 6 = 6$$

Grade 1                45                Chapter 15

---

Name _____

15-8

## Homework Practice

*Problem-Solving Investigation: Choose a Strategy*

**Choose a strategy and solve.**

| Problem Solving Strategies |
|---|
| • Guess and check |
| • Choose the operation |
| • Make a table |

1. Nick's teddy bear is 22 inches high. Fred's teddy bear is 10 inches high. How many inches taller is Nick's teddy bear?

   **12** inches

2. The classroom is 35 feet long. A shelf is 3 feet long. How much longer is the classroom than the shelf?

   **32** feet

3. Lisa has 32 marbles. Tim has 41 marbles. About how many marbles do they have? Round.

   About **70** marbles

4. Mr. Lin spends 40 cents at the store. He buys 2 objects. What does Mr. Lin buy? Circle your answer.

5. 21 birds are in a field. 18 more fly in. How many birds are there now?

   **39** birds

6. Jan has 12 red stickers and 31 yellow stickers. About how many stickers does she have? Round.

   About **40** stickers

Grade 1                44                Chapter 15

---

Answers

## 15-9 Reteach

Name _____

*Estimate Differences*

If you do not need an exact difference, you can estimate.

If a number ends in 5, 6, 7, 8, or 9, you can round up.

If a number ends in 0, 1, 2, 3, or 4, you can round down.

What is 26 − 13?

26 is about the same as 30.

13 is about the same as 10.

30 − 10 = 20, so the exact difference of 26 − 13 will be about 20.

**Round each number to the nearest ten. Then subtract.**

1. 59 rounds to **60**
   12 rounds to **10**
   59 − 12 is about **50**
   **60** − **10** = **50**

2. 28 rounds to **30**
   19 rounds to **20**
   28 − 19 is about **10**
   **30** − **20** = **10**

3. 42 rounds to **40**
   21 rounds to **20**
   42 − 21 is about **20**
   **40** − **20** = **20**

4. 67 rounds to **70**
   33 rounds to **30**
   67 − 33 is about **40**
   **70** − **30** = **40**

Grade 1    46    Chapter 15

---

## 15-9 Skills Practice

Name _____

*Estimate Differences*

**Round to the nearest *ten*. Then subtract. Use the number lines to help.**

(number lines: 10 11 12 13 14 15 16 17 18 19 20 21 22 23 24 25 26 27 28 29 30 and 30 31 32 33 34 35 36 37 38 39 40 41 42 43 44 45 46 47 48 49 50)

1. 39 − 32
   39 rounds to **40**
   32 rounds to **30**
   **40** − **30** = **10**

2. 48 − 24
   48 rounds to **50**
   24 rounds to **20**
   **50** − **20** = **30**

3. 47 − 28
   **50** − **30** = **20**

4. 49 − 17
   **50** − **20** = **30**

5. 38 − 21
   **40** − **20** = **20**

6. 43 − 14
   **40** − **10** = **30**

**Solve.**

7. Lily has 57 marbles. Her brother has 22 marbles. About how many more marbles does Lily have?
   **60** − **20** = **40**
   She has about **40** more marbles.

Grade 1    47    Chapter 15

# Answers (Lesson 15-9)

Name _____

## 15-9 Homework Practice
*Estimate Differences*

**Round to the nearest *ten*. Then subtract.**
**Use the number lines to help.**

30 31 32 33 34 35 36 37 38 39 40 41 42 43 44 45 46 47 48 49 50

50 51 52 53 54 55 56 57 58 59 60 61 62 63 64 65 66 67 68 69 70

1. 48 − 31
48 rounds to **50**
31 rounds to **30**
**50** − **30** = **20**

2. 67 − 43
67 rounds to **70**
43 rounds to **40**
**70** − **40** = **30**

3. 55 − 41
**60** − **40** = **20**

4. 68 − 39
**70** − **40** = **30**

5. 46 − 32
**50** − **30** = **20**

6. 68 − 42
**70** − **40** = **30**

**Solve.**

7. Ms. Green makes 65 cookies for the bake sale. She sells about 25. About how many cookies are left?

about **40** cookies

Name _____

## 15-9 Problem Solving Practice
*Estimate Differences*

**Estimate to solve.**

1. Cal has 21 cents. His brother has 9 cents. About how much more does Cal have?

**20** − **10** = **10**
Cal has about **10** cents more.

2. Ann has 47 game cards. She gives 21 cards to her friends. About how many cards does she have now?

**50** − **20** = **30**   She has about **30** cards.

3. Rosa runs for 45 minutes the first day. She runs 23 minutes the next day. She says she ran about 70 minutes in all.
Is she right? **Yes**

4. Jun's mom buys 45 apples. Jun eats 8 of them. About how many apples are left?

**50** − **10** = **40**
There are about **40** apples left.

5. Nate catches 28 fish. Tina catches 66 fish. Tina says she has about 50 more fish than Nate. Nate says she only has about 40 more.
Who is right? **Nate**

15-9

**Enrich**

*Skating into Estimation*

Name _____

**Round to solve the subtraction sentences.
Draw a line from the skater to the skateboard.**

about 60
about 50
about 40

about 10
about 20
about 30

87 − 31
82 − 41
59 − 53
54 − 32
67 − 21
43 − 12

50

Chapter 15

Grade 1

# Answers (Chapter Diagnostic Test and Chapter Pretest)

---

## Chapter Pretest

Name _____

**15**

### Chapter Pretest

**Add or subtract. Write your answer.**

1.  20
   + 50
   ____
    **70**

2.  60
   − 40
   ____
    **20**

3.  32
   + 4
   ____
    **36**

**Round to the nearest ten.**
**Then add or subtract.**
**Use the number line to help.**

20 21 22 23 24 25 26 27 28 29 30 31 32 33 34 35 36 37 38 39 40 41 42 43 44 45 46 47 48 49 50

4. 22 + 46   about **70**

5. 45 − 31   about **20**

6. 34 + 44   about **70**

7. 48 − 23   about **30**

**Solve.**

8. Jake rode his bike for 24 yards.
   Sara rode her bike for 32 yards.
   Jake says they rode 66 yards in all.
   Is he right?   **no**

---

## Chapter Diagnostic Test

Name _____

**15**

### Chapter Diagnostic Test
*Are You Ready for Chapter 15?*

**Write how many tens and ones.**

1.  **4** tens **3** ones = **43**

2.  **5** tens **6** ones = **56**

**Add or subtract.**

3.   8
    + 1
    ___
     **9**

4.  15
   − 9
   ___
    **6**

5.   6
    − 2
    ___
     **4**

6.  12
   − 5
   ___
    **7**

7.   9
    + 5
    ___
    **14**

**Write each number.**

8. 1 more than 25 is  **26**

9. 10 less than 40 is  **30**

10. 10 more than 40 is  **50**

11. 1 less than 60 is  **59**

**Answers**

# Answers (Mid-Chapter Test and Vocabulary Test)

## 15 Vocabulary Test

Name _____

**Write the correct word in the blank. Use the words from the box.**

| addends  estimate  sum  difference  add  subtract  round |

1. To **subtract** means to take away or find the difference.

2. To **add** means to find the total or the sum.

3. The answer to an addition problem is called the **sum** .

4. You can **estimate** if you do not need an exact number.

5. The answer to a subtraction problem is called the **difference** .

6. The numbers you add are called **addends** .

**Fill in the circle for the correct answer.**

7. In 31, which number is in the ones spot?
   ○ 3   conceptual error
   ● 1   correct answer
   ○ 2   conceptual error
   ○ 5   guess

8. In 52, which number is in the tens spot?
   ○ 2   conceptual error
   ○ 3   guess
   ○ 1   guess
   ● 5   correct answer

## 15 Mid-Chapter Test

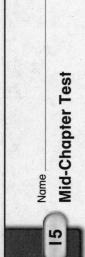

Name _____

**Add or subtract. Use □ if you want to.**

1. $\begin{array}{r} 20 \\ + 40 \\ \hline 60 \end{array}$   2. $\begin{array}{r} 50 \\ - 20 \\ \hline 30 \end{array}$   3. $\begin{array}{r} 21 \\ + 4 \\ \hline 25 \end{array}$

**Round to the nearest *ten*. Estimate the sum. Fill in the circle for the correct answer.**

20 21 22 23 24 25 26 27 28 29 30 31 32 33 34 35 36 37 38 39 40

4. 39 + 28
   ○ about 10   procedural error
   ● about 70   correct answer
   ○ about 67   conceptual error

**Fill in the circle for the correct answer.**

5. Boats in the race are 2 different colors. There are 15 boats. What colors are they? Use guess and check to solve.

5 red boats    10 tan boats    15 blue boats

The boats are
   ● red and tan   correct answer
   ○ tan and blue   guess
   ○ red and blue   guess
   ○ red, tan, and blue   conceptual error

# Answers (Oral and Listening Assessment Response Sheets)

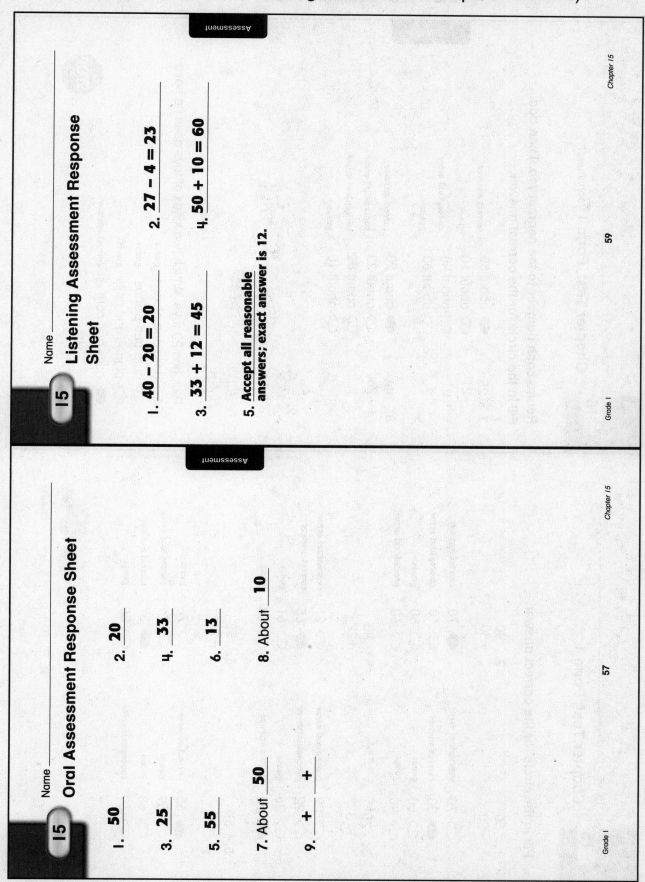

Name _____

## Listening Assessment Response Sheet

15

1. 40 − 20 = 20

2. 27 − 4 = 23

3. 33 + 12 = 45

4. 50 + 10 = 60

5. Accept all reasonable answers; exact answer is 12.

Chapter 15          59          Grade 1

Name _____

## Oral Assessment Response Sheet

15

1. 50

2. 20

3. 25

4. 33

5. 55

6. 13

7. About 50

8. About 10

9. ___ + ___

___ + ___

Chapter 15          57          Grade 1

Answers

# Answers (Chapter Test, Form I)

## 15  Name _____

### Chapter Test, Form I (continued)

Round each number to the nearest *ten.* Then add.
Fill in the circle for the correct answer.

7.  25
   +21

- ● about 50 — correct answer
- ○ about 10 — guess
- ○ about 45 — conceptual error
- ○ about 60 — guess

8.  48
   −26

- ● about 20 — correct answer
- ○ about 23 — conceptual error
- ○ about 80 — conceptual error
- ○ about 10 — guess

9.

dolls 15        cars 5        planes 10

Rick has 20 toys. Which two kinds of toys does he have?

- ○ dolls and planes — guess
- ○ cars and planes — guess
- ○ planes and dolls — guess
- ● dolls and cars — correct answer

---

## 15  Name _____

### Chapter Test, Form I

Fill in the circle for the correct answer.

1.  50
   −20

- ○ 70 — conceptual error
- ● 30 — correct answer
- ○ 50 — guess
- ○ 40 — guess

2.  40
   +30

- ● 70 — correct answer
- ○ 10 — conceptual error
- ○ 50 — guess
- ○ 60 — procedural error

3.  25
   + 3

- ○ 29 — procedural error
- ○ 22 — conceptual error
- ○ 26 — guess
- ● 28 — correct answer

4.  43
   +22

- ○ 21 — conceptual error
- ● 65 — correct answer
- ○ 61 — guess
- ○ 68 — guess

5.  67
   − 2

- ● 65 — correct answer
- ○ 59 — guess
- ○ 63 — guess
- ○ 69 — conceptual error

6.  58
   −21

- ○ 76 — guess
- ○ 79 — conceptual error
- ● 37 — correct answer
- ○ 35 — guess

GO on

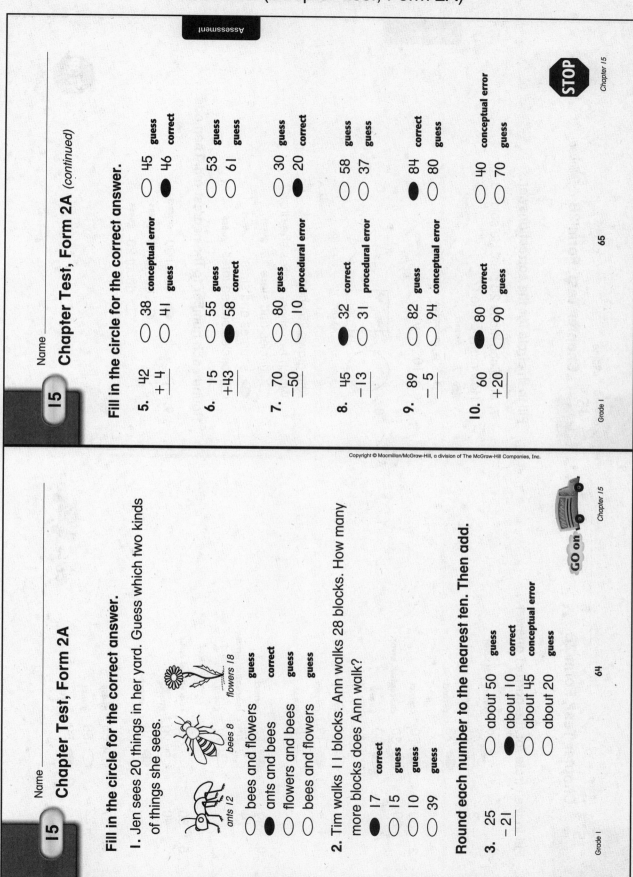

## 15 Chapter Test, Form 2A

Name _____

**Fill in the circle for the correct answer.**

1. Jen sees 20 things in her yard. Guess which two kinds of things she sees.

   ants 12   bees 8   flowers 18

   ○ bees and flowers — guess
   ● ants and bees — correct
   ○ flowers and bees — guess
   ○ bees and flowers — guess

2. Tim walks 11 blocks. Ann walks 28 blocks. How many more blocks does Ann walk?

   ● 17 — correct
   ○ 15 — guess
   ○ 10 — guess
   ○ 39 — guess

**Round each number to the nearest ten. Then add.**

3. $25 - 21$

   ○ about 50 — guess
   ● about 10 — correct
   ○ about 45 — conceptual error
   ○ about 20 — guess

GO on

Grade 1    64    Chapter 15

## 15 Chapter Test, Form 2A (continued)

Name _____

**Fill in the circle for the correct answer.**

5. $42 + 4$

   ○ 38 — conceptual error
   ○ 41 — guess
   ○ 45 — guess
   ● 46 — correct

6. $15 + 43$

   ○ 55 — guess
   ● 58 — correct
   ○ 53 — guess
   ○ 61 — guess

7. $70 - 50$

   ○ 80 — guess
   ○ 10 — procedural error
   ○ 30 — guess
   ● 20 — correct

8. $45 - 13$

   ● 32 — correct
   ○ 31 — procedural error
   ○ 58 — guess
   ○ 37 — guess

9. $89 - 5$

   ○ 82 — guess
   ○ 94 — conceptual error
   ● 84 — correct
   ○ 80 — guess

10. $60 + 20$

   ● 80 — correct
   ○ 90 — guess
   ○ 40 — conceptual error
   ○ 70 — guess

STOP

Grade 1    65    Chapter 15

# Answers (Chapter Test, Form 2B)

---

**Name**

## 15 Chapter Test, Form 2B (continued)

**Fill in th circle for the correct answer.**

**7.** Mr. Cobb made 20 pies. He sold 13.
How many are left?
- ● 7   **correct**
- ○ 33  **conceptual error**
- ○ 10  **guess**

**8.**
*circles 5    squares 10    stars 15*

Ann draws 25 shapes.
Which two shapes does she draw?
- ○ circles and stars    **guess**
- ● squares and stars    **correct**
- ○ circles and squares  **guess**

**Round each number to the nearest *ten*. Then add.**

**9.**  19
      +11
- ● about 30  **correct**
- ○ about 10  **guess**
- ○ about 20  **guess**

---

**Name**

## 15 Chapter Test, Form 2B

**Fill in the circle for the correct answer.**

**1.**  76
      − 3
- ○ 79  **conceptual error**
- ○ 71  **guess**
- ● 73  **correct**

**2.**  50
      +20
- ● 70  **correct**
- ○ 30  **conceptual error**
- ○ 80  **guess**

**3.**  15
      + 4
- ○ 11  **conceptual error**
- ● 19  **correct**
- ○ 18  **guess**

**4.**  39
      −14
- ● 25  **correct**
- ○ 54  **conceptual error**
- ○ 27  **guess**

**5.**  50
      −40
- ○ 90  **conceptual error**
- ○ 20  **guess**
- ● 10  **correct**

**6.**  37
      +22
- ○ 55  **guess**
- ○ 58  **guess**
- ● 59  **correct**

GO on

# Answers (Chapter Test, Form 2C)

**15**

Name _____

## Chapter Test, Form 2C

**Write your answer.**

1.
$$\begin{array}{r} 40 \\ -10 \\ \hline \mathbf{30} \end{array}$$

2.
$$\begin{array}{r} 50 \\ +40 \\ \hline \mathbf{90} \end{array}$$

3.
$$\begin{array}{r} 43 \\ +5 \\ \hline \mathbf{48} \end{array}$$

4.
$$\begin{array}{r} 51 \\ +37 \\ \hline \mathbf{88} \end{array}$$

5.
$$\begin{array}{r} 69 \\ -4 \\ \hline \mathbf{65} \end{array}$$

6.
$$\begin{array}{r} 87 \\ -44 \\ \hline \mathbf{43} \end{array}$$

GO on

---

**15**

Name _____

## Chapter Test, Form 2C *(continued)*

**Round each number to the nearest *ten*. Write your answer.**

7.
$$\begin{array}{r} 43 \\ +22 \\ \hline \text{about } \mathbf{60} \end{array}$$

8.
$$\begin{array}{r} 75 \\ -34 \\ \hline \text{about } \mathbf{50} \end{array}$$

**Solve.**

9. Leo planted 17 seeds in his yard. Which two kinds of seeds did he use?

corn 12    peas 10    beets 7

**peas and beets**

**Put in the missing signs.**

10. $16 - 5 - 4 = 7$

STOP

# Answers (Chapter Test, Form 2D)

**15** Chapter Test, Form 2D *(continued)*

Name _____

**Write your answer.**

6. 13
  +15
  **28**

7. 44
  − 3
  **41**

8. 50
  −40
  **10**

9. 20
  +20
  **40**

10. 26
  + 3
  **29**

11. 38
  −15
  **23**

STOP

Chapter 15

Grade 1      71

---

**15** Chapter Test, Form 2D

Name _____

**Round each number to the nearest *ten*.**

1. 12
  +29
  about **40**

2. 38
  −16
  about **20**

3. 17
  +42
  about **60**

4. 52
  −22
  about **30**

**Solve.**

5. Rose draws 14 shapes. Which two shapes does she draw?

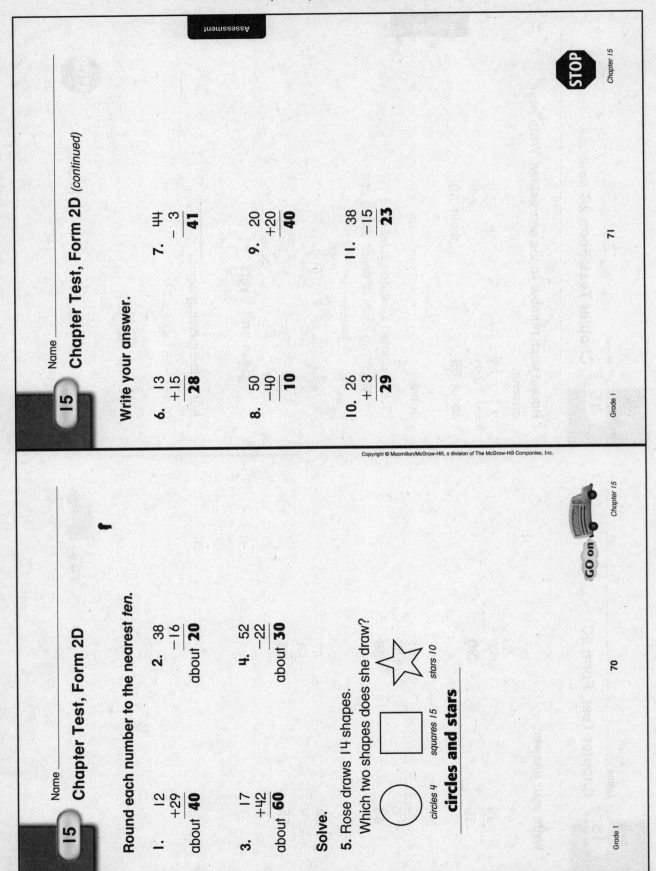

circles 4    squares 15    stars 10

**circles and stars**

GO on

Chapter 15

Grade 1      70

# Answers (Cumulative Test Practice Chapters 1–15)

Name _____

## 15  Cumulative Test Practice (continued)

**Fill in the circle for the correct answer.**

**10.** What comes next?

☆ ☆ ☆ ○

○ □ ☆ ☆ ☆
○ guess
○ conceptual error
● correct answer
○ guess

**11.** What time is it?

○ 12:00  procedural error
○ 14:30  guess
○ 6:00  guess
● 12:30  correct answer

**12.** What is this object called?

○ square  guess
○ sphere  guess
● cube  correct answer
○ triangle  guess

**STOP**

Name _____

## 15  Cumulative Test Practice Chapters 1–15

**Write the correct answer.**
**Add or subtract to solve.**

**1.**
```
  5
  2
+ 4
───
 11
```

**2.**
```
 10
−10
───
  0
```

**3.**
```
  7
− 0
───
  7
```

**4.**
```
  4
+ 8
───
 12
```

**5.**
```
  5
  5
+ 1
───
 11
```

**6.**
```
 49
−24
───
 25
```

**Count the coins. Write the value.**

**7.** = __82__ cents

**Count by 5s. Write the numbers.**

**8.** 5, 10, __15__, 20, __25__, __30__, 35

**Write the numbers in order.**

**9.** 13, 10, 47, 8, 81, 49

__8__, __10__, __13__, __47__, __49__, __81__

**GO on**

Assessment

Answers

# Answers (End-of-Year Test)

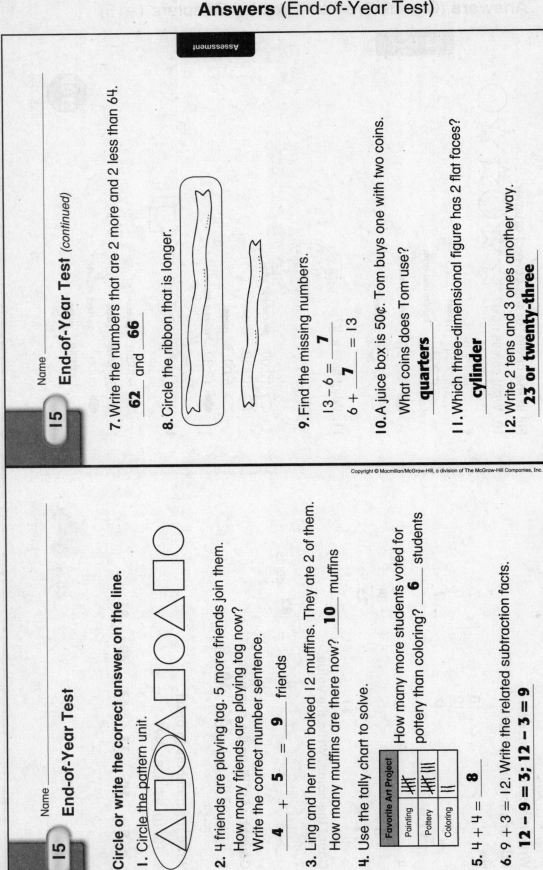

## 15 End-of-Year Test (continued)

Name _____

**7.** Write the numbers that are 2 more and 2 less than 64.

**62** and **66**

**8.** Circle the ribbon that is longer.

**9.** Find the missing numbers.

$13 - 6 = $ **7**

$6 + $ **7** $ = 13$

**10.** A juice box is 50¢. Tom buys one with two coins. What coins does Tom use?

**quarters**

**11.** Which three-dimensional figure has 2 flat faces?

**cylinder**

**12.** Write 2 tens and 3 ones another way.

**23 or twenty-three**

75    Chapter 15

GO on

## 15 End-of-Year Test

Name _____

**Circle or write the correct answer on the line.**

**1.** Circle the pattern unit.

**2.** 4 friends are playing tag. 5 more friends join them. How many friends are playing tag now? Write the correct number sentence.

**4** + **5** = **9** friends

**3.** Ling and her mom baked 12 muffins. They ate 2 of them. How many muffins are there now? **10** muffins

**4.** Use the tally chart to solve.

| Favorite Art Project | |
| --- | --- |
| Painting | 卌 |
| Pottery | 卌 Ⅲ |
| Coloring | Ⅱ |

How many more students voted for pottery than coloring? **6** students

**5.** $4 + 4 = $ **8**

**6.** $9 + 3 = 12$. Write the related subtraction facts.

**12 − 9 = 3; 12 − 3 = 9**

74    Chapter 15

GO on

# Answers (End-of-Year Test)

## 15 — End-of-Year Test (continued)

Name _____

**19.** Tim counts by fives. Write the numbers he missed:

5, 10, **15**, 20, **25**, 30

**20.** Circle the one that holds the *most*.

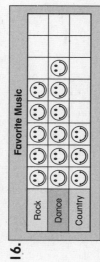

**21.** Circle the numbers you add first. Then find the sum.

(3 + 5) + 7 = **15**

**22.** Elena buys an orange. She spends 3 nickels and 3 pennies. How much does the orange cost?

**18** ¢

**23.** Chen draws a shape that has no sides. What shape does Chen draw?

**circle**

**24.** 
$$\begin{array}{r} 71 \\ -\ 5 \\ \hline \mathbf{66} \end{array}$$

---

## 15 — End-of-Year Test (continued)

Name _____

**13.** Circle your answer. 15 _____ 10

(is greater than (>))   is less than (<)   is equal to (=)

**14.**

Draw dots to show 5 + 0 = 5.

**15.** There are 5 birds in a nest. 2 fly away. How many birds are in the nest now?

**3** birds

**16.**

| Favorite Music | | | | |
|---|---|---|---|---|
| Rock | 😊 | 😊 | 😊 | |
| Dance | 😊 | 😊 | 😊 | 😊 |
| Country | 😊 | 😊 | 😊 | |

Which music has the most votes? **dance**

**17.** Kim's dog has 3 spots. Jose's dog has 7 spots. How many total spots do the dogs have?

**3** + **7** = **10** spots

**18.** Use the number line to help you solve.

0 1 2 3 4 5 6 7 8 9 10

8 − 5 = **3**

Answers